OWN Y...

HEALTH

LIKE YOUR LIFE
DEPENDS ON IT

OWN YOUR

HEALTH

LIKE YOUR LIFE
DEPENDS ON IT

IRENE WARD

Own Your Health Like Your Life Depends On It
First published in Great Britain in 2022 by
LOTUS BOOKS
An imprint of PARTNERSHIP PUBLISHING

Written by Irene Ward
Copyright © Irene Ward 2022

The information given in this book should not be treated as a substitute for professional advice. Any use of information in this book is at the reader's discretion and risk. Neither the author nor the publisher can be held responsible for any use, or misuse, of the suggestions made or for any material on third party websites.

All material used for this book is from the Author's memory and personal history. This book is based on the true life, recollections, and experiences of the author, seen through the eyes of a retired professional.

A CIP catalogue record for this book is available from the British Library.
ISBN 978-1-915200-32-7

Book cover design by: Michelle Miller & Partnership Publishing

Book typeset by:
PARTNERSHIP PUBLISHING
North Lincolnshire, United Kingdom

www.partnershippublishing.co.uk
Printed in England

Partnership Publishing is committed to a sustainable future for our business, our readers, and our planet; an organisation dedicated to promoting responsible management of forest resources. This book is made from paper certified by the Forestry Stewardship Council (FSC) an organisation dedicated to promoting responsible management of forest resources.

We operate a distinctive and ethical publishing philosophy in all areas of our business, from our global network of Authors to production and worldwide distribution.

I would like to dedicate this book to my wonderful family and friends, and all of the people who suffer unwittingly.

I'd also like to thank Mary and Henry for their help and enthusiasm for this book.

CONTENTS

INTRODUCTION

Like many people, I have taken the odd sickie or made excuses to friends that I am unwell to get me out of doing something that I am not in the mood for at that time. To be honest, when we opt out, it can sometimes be beneficial to both yourself and your employer. You are no good in work if you really don't want to be there. A day off may be all you need to get yourself back in the right head space. Of course, this is not something that should be abused.

However, I know of several people who deliberately sabotage their own health. They may do this unknowingly, or for reasons known only to them.

I have written this book to endeavour to understand the reasons why people sabotage their own health. I will be looking at why people don't adhere to special diets when they have a specific health problem that requires them to do so. I am also interested in why people abuse alcohol. There are many other ways people sabotage their health and some of these will be discussed also.

I will be taking a snapshot of each problem, as they could *easily* be the subject of a book individually.

People may recognise some traits they have, and they may endeavour to change their behaviour. I will be offering ways in which people can change their behaviour and offer some resources to allow them to live their best life.

By using scenarios, I will show how beliefs that develop from our programming **can** and **do** affect our daily lives.

We develop our identities around such beliefs, 'I am a good person' or 'I am not good enough.' That voice in your mind telling you, you are whatever you perceive yourself to be… ***whether this is true or not***. We often see ourselves differently to how others see us. Sometimes this can be very disconcerting, to find a lifelong friend has an opinion of you that you didn't realise. However, you can untangle these beliefs and re-programme your way of thinking.

Maybe relatives or friends of someone with sabotaging behaviour can offer help after reading this book.

Mental health will always be instrumental in self-sabotage, however, it's the age-old question: What came first, the chicken or the egg? Poor mental well-being, or did you have poor phsyical health first and that is why you behave the way you do?

In some of the scenarios, I will be looking at how emotions may affect our decisions - how we can become depressed because of ill health that may have been preventable.

Would people do things differently if they knew the consequences of their behaviour and could turn back time?

Even though my career was in general nursing, I have always found matters of the mind intriguing. It is this fascination and observation of people that provoked me to delve further into the reasons that people give for sabotaging their health and how they can be taught to change their behaviour.

When I studied hypnotherapy, I had no idea how it would help me in so many aspects of my own life. Although this book will touch on learning from hypnotherapy, it is in no way a book about hypnotherapy.

One of the first things we were taught in hypnotherapy is that the mind is in two thoughts; hence the saying, 'I am in two minds.' What this means is that your subconscious mind is battling with your conscious mind.

Dr David Servan-Schreiber (2005) explained, 'Inside the brain is a true brain, an emotional brain.' This second brain is built differently. It has a different cellular organisation, and it even has biochemical properties that are different from the rest of the neocortex, the most evolved part of the brain and the centre of language and thought.

I believe we should all take care of our health. I believe we have a responsibility to ourselves and others to be in the best health that we can be, whether we are able-bodied or disabled - whether we have chronic health problems or a common cold. To me this means eating healthily, having alcohol in moderation, taking exercise, and taking care of your mental wellbeing. This may all sound trite, and it is what health professionals are telling us to do but for some, this way of life eludes them. Some have gone down a path of self-destruction, and for some they see no way out, or have irreversible damage.

I aim to enable those who have become stuck in self-sabotage to find a way out.

Whoever said 'we are all born equal' is living in cloud cuckoo land. Even those born in the same household, to the same parents can be very different. We all have different traits and characters. Therefore, we respond differently to divergent situations. We all have different likes and dislikes; in fact, we are unique.

Even identical twins have variant traits. This is what makes us so fascinating.

I am not going to explore complex mental health problems and this book is not aimed at the scholar studying psychology. It is aimed at the 'average Joe.'

I am using people with different problems to identify why and how they sabotage their health. Some of the reasons will be the same. However, they will all use different ways to damage their health. Some of the remedies to improve their health will also be the same. Those with addiction obviously must give up the addiction in order for their health to improve, but different addictions require particular interventions.

I aim to show how everyday ordinary people sabotage their health and some of the time they either don't care or don't realise what they are doing to themselves. I am sure if we were asked if we could turn back time, there would be something we would all do differently.

Be kind to yourself

Don't try to fit in, to be normal: normal doesn't exist. Don't be afraid to be yourself. Don't try to please everyone, (you will never accomplish that) you just set yourself up to fail.

Don't wait until you are old and experienced to feel comfortable in your own skin.

Be proud of who you are and what you have achieved thus far.

Have dreams and goals, and don't be afraid to reach for the stars.

Don't keep putting things off. There is never a perfect time, there will always be something to get in the way.

Don't let anyone else put you off achieving your goals.

Do not allow yourself to be bullied. If you aren't strong enough to stand up to the bully, find someone who can.

It shouldn't take a tragedy in life to make you realise how precious and wonderful life is.

Being **HAPPY** matters. Happiness truly is a state of mind, remind yourself that you deserve to be happy just as much as the next person. If you need to change things in your life in order to be happy, what are you waiting for? Life is short and as someone said, 'this is not a rehearsal... you only get one shot, and then it's gone.'

You have the power to be the best you can be. Only *you* can do this, although you may require some encouragement or help, you mustn't be afraid to ask. The majority of people really do want to help. Anybody who doesn't isn't worth wasting your precious time on.

Do things that make you happy. Only you know what that might be. Make a list of happy places, happy activities, happy people etc. Use this tool when you begin to feel down. Don't wait until you are in a deep dark place. But if you are in that place, make sure you take steps NOW to get out of it.

Above all,

LOVE YOURSELF and BE TRUE TO YOURSELF.

ALISON'S STORY

SMOKING

Alison started smoking when she was sixteen. She is now in her late fifties and has health problems due to her smoking habit. She has tried many times to break the habit. However, she enjoys smoking and believes it helps her when she is stressed. Alison's family constantly plead with her to give up smoking. Her daughter is expecting her first baby and she is worried her mother won't be in good enough health to enjoy spending time with the child.

Alison's family have all commented on the odour of stale tobacco on her clothes, in the car, and in her home. Although this upsets Alison, she also becomes very angry and defensive about this.

Alison has Chronic Obstructive Pulmonary Disease (COPD). She also has peripheral vascular disease which led to her first heart attack. She has been advised by many health professionals to stop smoking. She takes numerous medications to try to improve her health. Alison finds it difficult when she has a chest infection to perform her daily activities. She often stays in her pyjamas all day because she doesn't have the energy to dress. She develops vascular ulcers on her lower legs from time to time. These take longer and longer to heal each time she has them.

People who smoke are four times more likely to develop heart disease. The reduction of oxygen increases the heart rate, therefore putting more stress on the heart. According to the NHS (2019), one in five deaths from heart disease is related to smoking.

Smoking is very addictive. Cigarettes contain nicotine, which is highly addictive. Nicotine alters the balance of two chemicals in your brain: dopamine and noradrenaline. When nicotine changes the levels of these chemicals, your mood and concentration levels change. Many smokers find this enjoyable. As with most drugs, the more you use them, the more you need to increase the use to get the same effect. If you try to give up nicotine with no substitute, it can make you feel anxious, depressed, and irritable. It can be difficult to quit using just your will power as nicotine cravings can be really strong. Studies by the NHS show that you are more likely to succeed if you get help from the NHS.

Smoking has affected Alison's appearance - her skin is sallow and very lined for her age, especially around her mouth. Her hair is thinning and is lifeless. Her teeth are stained. Cigarette smoke contains carbon monoxide which depletes the oxygen in your skin, and nicotine reduces blood flow, leaving skin dry and discoloured. Cigarette smoke also depletes many nutrients including vitamin C, which helps protect and repair the skin.

There are many other associated problems related to smoking that Alison could easily develop in the future. According to the NHS (2019), smoking increases your risk of developing more than fifty serious health conditions. Cancer is the most obvious health condition that Alison should be concerned about.

Smoking causes around 7 out of every 10 cases of lung cancer. However, lung cancer is just one of many types of cancer that smoking can cause. Smoking increases your risk of developing a stroke. I won't talk about every problem that smoking can cause as it is not the aim of this book. You can look at the NHS website to educate yourself on this. However, I will mention that there are risks of problems during pregnancy, associated with both smoking and passive smoking. Babies and young children are more likely to develop lung disease when they are subjected to passive smoking.

Alison will have to consider this when her daughter has the baby. Her daughter may already be thinking this as she is very insistent that her mother gives up smoking.

As previously mentioned, Alison had tried several times to give up smoking. She needs to get in the right frame of mind and really want to do it for herself. Giving up smoking is one of the best things anyone can do for their health. She has experienced this in the past and knows it is not going to be easy.

Support from friends, family and probably a health professional will give her extra support. Alison knows she will have withdrawal symptoms. When she has tried to stop smoking in the past, she found it extremely difficult and the thought of going through that again filled her with dread. Concern that she would fail again put her off. Cutting down on the number of cigarettes she smokes was something else she had also tried. However, she finds that she smokes almost absent minded and before she realises, she has smoked another packet.

The high price of cigarettes is another reason why she would like to give up smoking. She promised herself if they ever cost ten pounds for a packet of twenty, she would definitely give up. The brand she smokes cost twelve pounds sixty pence. Her aim to save for a holiday was supposed to encourage her. The price went up and up, but Alison's will power just wasn't strong enough. Sometimes when she thought of the lovely holiday she could have had, it made her miserable.

These highly unpleasant sensations arise within approximately two hours of her last cigarette and include:

- Irritability.
- Fatigue.
- Mood swings.
- Insomnia.
- Poor concentration.
- Headaches.
- Increased appetite.
- Anxiety.
- Depression.

Is it any wonder people find it difficult to stop smoking? Alison will undoubtedly require some form of nicotine replacement. She will be able to get advice from her GP for this.

What I want to know is why anybody would choose to deliberately harm themselves by taking up such a destructive habit in the first place?

Having asked many smokers and those who have managed to quit, they all have a common theme. They started smoking at a young, impressionable age when peer pressure was important to them. They wanted to appear older and feel part of a social group. Some people said, they started to smoke only when they went out drinking and from then, have smoked more and more but still associate smoking with alcohol. When trying to give up, the hardest part was when they went out socialising.

Many people said, they use smoking to relieve stress. When they are in work, it gives them an excuse to take a break away from the work environment. They feel refreshed and ready to continue after a smoke break.

Once they had started, they found the pleasure or the rush that smoking gave them only meant they wanted more. Nicotine is both a stimulant and a sedative, and like many drugs, it gives you a variety of different feelings.

Whatever the reason for starting smoking, that reason is certainly not the reason you have continued to smoke. Smoking is highly addictive, and your choice to smoke is no longer relevant. Don't minimise the seriousness of the danger of smoking just because millions of people do it, and it is legal.

Every breath of clean fresh air you take in is filled with life-giving oxygen, nitrogen, and other gasses. Whereas tobacco smoke that you are filling your lungs with, is filled with poisonous chemicals and gasses, including tar, carbon monoxide, and carcinogenic hydrocarbons.

I hope Alison is successful in her endeavour to give up smoking. I know she wishes she had never started smoking. I stated that Alison would require a nicotine substitute to enable her to quit. However, I believe that hypnotherapy would increase her chances of giving up tremendously.

Hypnotherapy would put Alison back in control and give her the belief that she can do it. It would increase her self-esteem and give her the tools to remain a non-smoker. Hypnotherapy would build Alison's willpower. However, for hypnotherapy to be successful, the person has to want to do it for themselves and not because someone else wants them to.

Alison said, she would never have started smoking if she realised what it was going to do to her health. Because she can't see or feel the effects of smoking with each individual cigarette, she hasn't realised the accumulative effect. She thought smoking used to relieve stress but now she realises it actually *causes* her stress. For example - the cost of them, the concerns when she has run out of them, the upset it causes her family, not to mention the harm she is doing to her health.

If you are a smoker or someone you care about is, then for the sake of your health, <u>stop smoking</u>.

<u>Resources to help give up smoking:</u>

www.nhs.uk/quit_smoking/nhs
www.nicorette.co.uk/
www.blf.org.uk – British Lung Foundation
http://smokefree.gov
www.cancerresearchuk.org

ETHAN'S
STORY

DIABETES

Ethan is a 42-year-old married man. He has 3 children aged four years, two and a half years, and twelve months. He works as an electrician.

Sometimes his work can be quite physical. He finds himself struggling as he is overweight. He is very tired when he gets home from work and his marriage is steadily declining as his wife also works and does everything for the children. She gets angry because he doesn't have the energy to help around the house. Ethan also finds that his love life is, in his words, 'going down the pan.'

So, there are several issues that Ethan must deal with if he is to improve his overall quality of life. If Ethan were to lose weight, this may reverse his diabetes, which may increase his libido and help with his fatigue.

First and foremost, he needs to address his lifestyle. Ethan has always had a sweet tooth. As a child, food was given as a treat and a reward. Therefore, not only was his sweet tooth gratified, but the feelgood endorphins would also kick in. As parents we should be mindful of this. If children see food {especially sweet treats} as a reward, this may become habit forming. As responsible parents, we should try to use other ways of rewarding our children. For example, a day out or a book or for a quick reward/treat - some fruit.

Ethan has been overweight for most of his life. He has tried to diet. He is the worst kind of dieter as he yo-yo diets. When weight loss is drastic, it is usually regained quickly. If a healthy, well-balanced diet is eaten, then weight loss will be slow and steady. Dieting in this healthy way, that may also be supported by a health professional or slimming club, will ensure a greater possibility of success. This is more of a lifestyle change than a faddy diet. It is well documented that yo-yo dieting throws off your gut bacteria, which may lead to gastrointestinal conditions, such as inflammatory bowel disease and obesity.

We all know that junk food is bad for us. It provides instant gratification, is high in calories, and leaves us feeling sleepy and sluggish. Unfortunately, fast food is engineered to taste good. Some people tend to over-indulge in poor eating habits. This can affect every organ in your body. It can dampen your mood and make you irritable. It will make you put on weight, and because you are not giving your body the nutrients it requires, it can make you vulnerable to illness and disease.

Diabetes doesn't just affect the person with diabetes, it can affect the whole family and also friends. Ethan knows his uncontrolled diabetes is affecting his relationship with his wife. He will need to act very soon and ensure his wife is on board with the changes he needs to make.

Diabetes, of course, causes anxiety for the person who is affected, but it often causes anxiety for those around them. It can be very stressful knowing that someone you care for is deliberately harming themselves by not adhering to the advice given by the health professionals. It is difficult for Ethan because his wife is constantly berating him for not keeping his blood glucose levels under control. This puts a strain on the relationship. However, Ethan points out that his wife is the one who predominately does the shopping and meal planning. He thinks she shouldn't buy cakes, biscuits, and the like. However, she insists that her and the children shouldn't have to deprive themselves because he can't control himself.

Ethan feels embarrassed when they eat out as his wife points out 'he can't eat that.' Ethan feels he is being monitored all the time and the lecturing gets him down. When he is down, he turns to food for comfort. He tells himself, 'what the hell, just this once won't matter.' But of course, these occasions when he feels like this **do matter**. It is, so to speak, 'just another nail in his coffin.'

The first step to helping Ethan would be to get advice from his diabetic nurse. These nurses are specially trained to deal with all aspects of diabetes, including psychological and physical problems. They may advise Ethan to have an open and honest dialogue with his wife. Maybe some joint counselling would be required. There is obviously resentment on both sides and to solve the problems, sometimes a third party can help them to see the other person's point of view. After all, they both want the same thing. Arguments can lead to bad moods which may translate to the bedroom. Ethan has said his love life is being affected. However, he doesn't say whether it is being affected emotionally, physically, or both.

Ethan's wife may need advice on healthy eating, perhaps some diet sheets. She may not know how to support Ethan, and instead of being the wife who constantly nags, maybe she could help get his blood glucose under control and see it more as a joint/family duty of care. Although Ethan requires support, he must take responsibility for his own health. He needs to be honest with himself and not rely on others.

Over time, if Ethan doesn't maintain a healthy eating regime and his glucose levels remain high, he may experience complications. Complications can be as serious as cardiovascular problems or nerve damage. Both have implications for sexual health and Ethan may not realise this.

Diabetes is also known to impact on mental health which in turn affects sexual health. Diabetes damages blood vessels which can affect blood flow to the penis. It also affects the nerves, therefore making it more difficult to maintain an erection. Ethan needs to '**own his health**' before it is too late, and his poor health owns him.

In some cases, it is possible to put diabetes into remission by eating healthily and losing weight. There is no easy fix and no guarantee that diabetes can be reversed, but I know people who have been successful in doing this.

Storing too much fat in the pancreas and liver affects how type 2 diabetes develops, and losing this fat can help put your diabetes into remission. As previously mentioned, it's not just about dieting. It's about lifestyle changes forever that will improve your chance of reversing diabetes and improving your overall health.

With support of his family and friends, Ethan could really improve his overall health. If he doesn't tackle this now, he will slowly but surely see his health deteriorate. Diabetes causes so many non-reversable health problems that Ethan says he is going to really try, and his wife has also promised to help and support him.

When Ethan was asked, 'do you know how you got to this point where you are facing so many health and psychological problems?' he replied that it crept up on him and seemed to happen so quickly. He added that it scares him now, and he never thought things would get this bad. He is worried what the future holds and wishes he had never let it get this bad. He admits he feels ashamed and embarrassed. He can see that if he doesn't tackle the problem that he will deteriorate and he knows he is putting his marriage at risk. He wants to be a better husband and father. He wishes he knew at the beginning of his journey, when he was newly diagnosed, the devastating effect diabetes can have on all aspects of your life. He admitted he would definitely take on board the advice he was given by the health professionals.

He wishes he knew back then how much it would affect his family. He recommends that people research and find out as much as they can and the dire consequences of being blasé about diabetes. He thinks schools should get involved as diabetes is one of the biggest killers and is rapidly on the increase in the western world. He feels that a multidisciplinary approach to education in schools could help future generations avoid falling into the fast food and couch-potato trap.

Prevention is certainly better than cure and could help save lives and help save the NHS a lot of money.

Resources to help diabetics:

www.diabetes.org.uk/
www.nhs.uk/diabetes.uk

AMELIA'S
STORY

CERVICAL CANCER

Amelia is forty-five years old and a mother of two children. She works full time as a police officer. She has a very busy lifestyle and according to her, a very healthy lifestyle. She has an athletic build and enjoys running most days. Running reduces her stress levels and increases her stamina.

She loves her job and is determined to climb the ladder when the children are a bit older. Her friend group have been together (most of them) since school. Her husband Mark is also a police officer, and they enjoy banter about their work. They are a great support for one another because they understand the stress and strains of the job. Their marriage is strong, and they share many interests, although they both have their own space and hobbies.

Amelia enjoys yoga and meditation. Her stress management is as good as it can be given the work she does and her shift patterns. They enjoy a social drink but neither of them drinks to excess. Amelia very rarely attends her GP surgery because 'she is just never ill.'

However, her world was turned upside down when she received a diagnosis of cervical cancer. The cancer was advanced, and she had metastases by the time she noticed symptoms. Amelia had never been for a cervical smear test, by her own admittance she said, 'she didn't have time and felt it would never happen to her.'

The first signs of anything being amiss was when her periods became heaver and irregular, but she still dismissed the signs, and thought it may be an early menopause.

It was her husband Mark who persuaded her to seek medical help. She was embarrassed and it took Mark some time to explain that if it was a problem, the earlier she sought help, there would be a better chance of it getting sorted.

Amelia was actually terrified but went to her general practitioner. Her GP took a history and asked Amelia what had brought her to the surgery. Amelia told him that her periods had become heavy and that she put it down to the menopause, but that she was now experiencing some other symptoms. She said that she was worried and that she hadn't been for a smear test.

Her GP reassured her but pressed her for further information. Amelia went on to say that she had some pain and slight bleeding following intercourse. Her GP suggested that rather than have a smear test, that because of her symptoms it may be more prudent to have a referral for a colposcopy.

A colposcopy, he went on to explain to her, would look for abnormal cells on her cervix and because a biopsy could be taken at the same time, it may save her having to come back to the clinic.

Amelia decided that she would go for the colposcopy. She told Mark and he was very supportive. They decided that until they knew what they were dealing with, they wouldn't tell the children. However, Amelia wanted to tell her Mum because she had been telling her Mum some of her symptoms and she was a great support.

The results were that Amelia did indeed have cancer cells. She would have to have further tests to see if the cancer had spread. She had already had blood tests at the GP surgery. These tests were to assess her liver function, kidneys, and her bone marrow.

Amelia felt like she was on a roller coaster and not one that she wanted to be on. She went through the 'why me?' - the guilt for not ever having a smear test. The; 'what if anything happens to me, how will Mark cope?' questions, whizzing round and round in her head, making her feel dizzy. Her world was turned upside down. So many questions and yet she felt no answers coming her way.

Then, she had a call from a Macmillan nurse who introduced herself as Jan. She asked if Amelia would like to have a chat. Amelia's sense of relief was palpable. Amelia soon struck up a good rapport with Jan. She felt that while Jan was very knowledgeable, she was down to earth and friendly.

Little did Amelia know that Jan would become a very important person through her journey with cancer.

Amelia underwent many diagnostic procedures. She also had several treatment interventions. This part of Amelia's journey is distressing in parts, and I have therefore decided to omit them. I felt it had no bearing on the reason for writing this chapter of my book.

I am focusing on why Amelia didn't attend her regular smear tests and what Amelia can do to ease the phycological and physical pain of cancer, not only on herself, but her family.

According to Cancer Research UK, there are several barriers to cervical cancer screening. They include the reasons that Amelia gave and some others too. They say that Ethnic minority women are less likely to attend screening because of a lack of understanding and awareness of what the screening is for and why they need it. Cancer Research UK suggest, all women regardless of ethnicity, admit that fear, embarrassment, shame, lack of time, low perceived risk and an absence of symptoms were the main barriers.

Amelia is in the 9% of women aged between 25-64 years who have never been screened.

Negative experiences were also given as a barrier to repeat attendance. Yet according to Jo's cervical cancer trust, screening can prevent up to 75% of all cervical cancer from developing. The NHS screening programme saves around 5,000 lives a year.

A survey undertaken by King Edward V11 hospital shows that cervical screening rates are at their lowest in two decades. The NHS has recently warned that missed smear appointments during the Covid 19 pandemic are creating a large backlog, which is putting extra pressure on the service.

Amelia is one of 220,000 women diagnosed with cervical cell changes every year, and of those, 3,000 women in the UK are told they have cancer. There are around 850 deaths from cervical cancer in the UK every year.

Amelia said she felt stupid because she didn't know how important having this screening was until it was too late. Unfortunately, Amelia passed away aged forty-seven years leaving two children and her husband Mark.

Amelia had some long chats with Jan the Macmillan nurse, and she asked Jan if there was any way she could help other women realise that the screening could save their lives? She also wanted to tell them how she could make it easier for women and less embarrassing to attend the appointments. So, Amelia's legacy are ways in which the test can be made more comfortable for women.

She explained, you should wear comfortable clothes that help you feel at ease, bearing in mind that you will be lying on your back with your knees raised in order for the test to be carried out.

- A dress or skirt that is loose fitting and can enable you to assume this position without taking it off is preferable to a tight skirt or jeans.

- You could ask for a woman to do the test if you feel more comfortable with that.

- Ask to change your position if you are uncomfortable.

- Bring a friend or partner to support you.

- Give yourself a treat afterwards.

- Remind yourself that it only takes a few minutes and could potentially save your life.

- If you are extremely embarrassed, try some relaxation techniques or hypnotherapy to get you through.

Resources for dealing with cancer:

Book your smear test at your GP surgery or online. You will be sent a letter inviting you. If you have not booked your appointment, don't wait until you receive another letter. Book your appointment right away.
www.macmillan.org.uk/
www.cancerresearchuk.org

ERIN'S
STORY

COERCIVE CONTROL

Erin is a young woman in her late thirties. She has two children, a son aged six and a daughter aged four. She married when she was twenty-five, and had her son when she was twenty-seven, her daughter followed two years later.

Her husband James is thirty-five. He is an accountant and is a partner in the company he works at. They met at a friend's summer barbeque. He was a handsome man who had lots of confidence. His cocky attitude and dry sense of humour was what Erin found attractive the moment they met. They spent the rest of the summer having fun. He played tennis and she soon took up the sport herself. She was happier than she had ever been.

James was very protective, and she found this appealing. He would help her decide what clothes to wear and how she wore her hair. She loved him with all her heart. The wedding was a small affair. They had decided to splash out on a wonderful honeymoon instead of (as James said) 'wasting money on a flash wedding, spending on people he didn't even know.'

Erin would have liked a few more family and friends at the wedding but she understood his logic. They enjoyed the honeymoon in the Maldives, but looking back, Erin noticed that everything they did was James's idea. Her ideas were always rejected by him. At this time, Erin didn't mind. She was so in love and James did have good taste.

Shortly after returning home from honeymoon, Erin realised that James wasn't domesticated at all. However, he expected the house to be immaculate at all times and a meal on the table when he got in from work. Not too unreasonable. However, Erin worked full time in a day centre for adults with learning disabilities. When she got home from work, she was exhausted. She tried her best to keep on top of the housework, but James was becoming more and more fastidious.

He was extremely untidy himself, and when she asked him to put his dirty clothes in the linen basket he would reply in a joking manner, 'that's what I got you for silly.' Once again, Erin thought she was being too sensitive and passed it off as a joke. All too soon, James was expecting more and more of Erin, and she was feeling frustrated and tired. James would regularly try to humiliate her when they were with friends. He would tell her she was becoming more like the people she worked with. This would upset Erin because she had the utmost respect and empathy for her clients. She had formed a bond with some of them. She thought to herself *'I'd rather be like them than like you.'*

As time passed, Erin became isolated. Following the birth of her children, she felt more alone than ever.

She joined mother and baby groups, but James would always discourage her, and eventually she would leave, for the sake of a quiet life. James knew where she was at all times. He put a tracker on her phone and her car. Erin was becoming more and more withdrawn. James would make fun of her. He would call her fat, even though she wasn't. He would tell her she ate too much. The physical abuse was no more than a shove or a slap. He didn't need to use his fists, he had complete control because of his bullying and aggressive behaviour.

Erin made excuses for him, telling herself and the few friends she had left that he was tired and stressed with work. She changed every aspect of her appearance - her actions and reactions to things. Her whole demeanour changed, from a bright bubbly personality to a shy withdrawn person. She only bought clothes approved by James. She felt like she was constantly walking on eggshells.

Although he had never been physically violent to the children, Erin tried to keep them quiet when he was around, for fear of annoying him. At times he would get so angry he would throw household objects around. Erin would rush around to make sure the house was clean and tidy for when he came home. She would be physically and mentally drained at bedtime. Even though she was exhausted, she found sleeping almost impossible. James would rape her almost every night and she had come to accept this, and just couldn't wait for it to be over so she could try to relax a little.

Erin lost a lot of weight, she stopped anything creative that she used to enjoy. She didn't read or listen to music anymore. Before meeting James, her creativity was something she was well known for. She was meticulous and took great pleasure in making wedding, christening, and other special occasion invitations for friends and family. She had a passion for making Christmas decorations and her eye for colour made her impeccable when it came to interior design.

One day, she hoped she would be able to take a course and pursue a career in that field. Although deep down in her heart, she knew she would never be able to do this if she stayed with James.

She found she was worrying excessively about even the smallest things. Physical symptoms began to appear, her hair was falling out. She found that she was suffering from muscle tension both night and day. She would wring her hands and clench her jaw to the point that in the morning, her jaw would be so painful she would need to take analgesia. Her neck and back muscles were constantly in knots. She had severe headaches. She was developing social anxiety because her self-esteem and confidence were so low. She even started to have panic attacks, especially in the evenings when the children had gone to bed. She felt cheated because this was supposed to be her time to relax.

However, the moment she let her guard down and she didn't have the children to distract her, her heart would race, she found her breathing would quicken. She felt an overpowering sense of doom, as though something dreadful was about to happen. A heavy pressure in her chest made her feel as though someone were pushing down on her.

Long-term effects of being in any kind of abusive relationship can be:

- Anxiety
- Chronic pain
- Guilt
- Insomnia
- Social withdrawal
- Chronic fatigue syndrome
- Fibromyalgia
- Eating disorders
- Headaches
- Heart disease
- Mental health issues
- Substance misuse
- Alcoholism
- Self-harm
- Nervous breakdown
- Gastrointestinal upset/stomach ulcers

Controlling behaviour can be a range of acts designed to make a person subordinate or dependent. This is usually done by isolating them from sources of support. They may deprive the person of the means to support themselves.

A controlling person will regulate behaviour, and this may be very subtle in the beginning. According to Timothy J. Legg PhD CRNP, there are twelve signs of a controlling personality:

1. Blaming you
2. Constant criticism
3. Keeping score
4. Creating drama
5. Intimidation
6. Moodiness
7. Ignoring boundaries
8. Jealousy
9. Attempting to change you
10. Abusive behaviour
11. Gaslighting
12. Asserting dominance

Erin felt trapped. She spoke with a friend who suggested counselling. Her sessions would have to be when James was at work. She told the counsellor that the reason she felt unable to leave her husband was that she didn't want to break up the family, although she was feeling that this was no longer as important to her. She thought she wouldn't be able to cope on her own. Erin worried most of all about custody of the children and what James might do when she wasn't there to protect them.

She had very real financial concerns. Even though she knew she could go back to work, she wouldn't be able to earn a high wage because, although she had a lot of experience, she didn't have any written qualifications. Childcare would have to be paid for because Erin couldn't rely on her elderly parents. She had concerns about where they would live. She was fearful that if she told James she was leaving, he may become violent. The stress of divorce and going to court terrified her, and where would she get the money to pay for legal fees? She felt overwhelmed by the mere thought of it. She continued to be downtrodden every day.

Eventually, after months of counselling and talking with her friend, she decided she could no longer live like this and even though she was terrified, she decided to leave James.

Initially, she went to stay with her friend. Eventually, she was offered a small house, rented from a housing association.

Erin found the courage to leave James because she didn't want the children to believe that her relationship was normal. She didn't want her lovely son to grow up to be like his father and she didn't want her daughter to think it was ok to be treated so badly. She felt a huge responsibility to leave before the children became influenced by their father.

Erin noticed how the children would pick up on James' mood and most of the time, they would alter their behaviour, but sometimes when they didn't, Erin would feel extremely anxious. She also noticed her son picking up on the tension and she could see that he was frightened.

Erin hated the effect that James was having on the children. She didn't want them to see the fear in her eyes. Erin could already tell the children were subjected to the coercive control. Erin realised that over the years, she had changed, and she hated herself. She hated her weakness. She hated the constant tension in the home. She hated the lack of social interaction. She hated the way her health was suffering. But most of all, she hated James. She hated him being near her and even the anticipation of him coming home.

Erin knew it was now or never. She wanted a better life for herself and her children. She felt that she still had a lot of years ahead of her, and that she could build a new life for her little family. It took courage and as

Erin said, 'sometimes you have to reach rock bottom before you realise that you have to make a better life, because no one else is going to do it for you.'

Although her physical and mental health had deteriorated and at times Erin blamed herself, once she was away from James's influence, and with the help of counselling, she realises she was not to blame. Understanding why Erin stayed with James until she reached rock bottom, may be difficult for some people. However, many people will be able to relate to her situation to a greater or lesser degree.

Belief in herself was what eventually gave Erin the strength and courage to leave James. Although she had become insecure while she was with him, she was raised to have self- respect. If she could turn back time, she would probably have left James before they had children. But she adored her children and if nothing else good came from her relationship, at least she had them.

Here are some helpful resources for anyone in a coercive relationship:

www.womensaid.org.uk
www.citizensadvice.org.uk have a national domestic abuse helpline. Its free phone 24-hour service providing advice and support. They can refer to emergency accommodation.

www.refuge.org.uk has lots of information and other useful websites for different groups e.g., teenagers, men, women, black women, rape crisis and many more.

There are many victim support organisations. They can offer advice on how to leave a relationship.

www.supportline.org is a group for lonely adults.

VIOLET'S
STORY

LONELINESS

Violet is 85 years old. She lives alone in a bungalow, surrounded by other elderly people. The community is very sociable. There is a community centre close-by and most of the residents attend luncheon clubs, bingo, early entertainment evenings, craft afternoons, and they can use the café to meet up and have a cuppa.

Violet is a sociable person and has made friends easily. She moved to the bungalow when her husband died. At first, she struggled, but soon found the community centre a hub of activity and everyone was friendly. Most of the ladies were in a similar position. There are several couples, and a few single men, some of these are widows. The gentlemen have also formed friendships. They enjoy afternoons playing cards or dominos and have formed teams where they play at local darts tournaments.

In 2020, the world was thrown into chaos when Covid 19 hit. We were initially told it was just like flu and we were concerned but didn't think it was so serious. Then as time went on, the number of people dying was becoming very concerning. There were daily government updates as this virus was spreading like wildfire. Violet's community were particularly worried because the death toll was rising, and the deaths were predominantly elderly people or those at risk from underlying health conditions. Everyone that Violet knew in her community had underlying health conditions, so they were very frightened.

The community centre closed and became a centre for testing those with symptoms to see if they had the virus. Violet was told by her family not to go shopping and not to mix with others. The only link she had to the outside world was the television and her phone. She didn't know how to use social media and her phone was very basic because she got confused with anything that was too complicated. Her food was delivered by the supermarket or her daughter (who wouldn't come inside, for fear of passing on the virus). The news was getting worse every day, and she watched Boris Johnson (UK Prime Minister at the time) deliver advice that seemed to change so often, she couldn't remember what she should or shouldn't be doing.

Violet's eldest daughter who lived in Scotland was living with different rules to those in England. Wales also had different rules. On March 26th, 2020, the UK introduced the first lockdown restrictions. Only essential shops could open. All hospitality was closed.

There were very few flights allowed in or out of the country. These new laws were being introduced all over the world at different times. All health care systems were struggling. Those health care professionals dealing with patients diagnosed with Covid 19 had to wear full PPE (personal protective equipment). There wasn't enough PPE to go around, and Doctors and Nurses were at very high risk of contracting Covid 19.

Politicians and health advisors were telling everyone to wear masks and keep a two-meter social distance. There were rules about how many people could meet outdoors. Rules about wearing a mask were confusing. Some guidance was that they were a waste of time, other government advisors were saying it prevented the transmission by reducing the respiratory particles in the air.

Violet has two daughters. Her eldest daughter in Scotland only saw Violet a couple of times a year. The visits would usually coincide with special occasions. There had been two such occasions when her daughter couldn't visit, and Violet wondered if she would ever see her again. Her other daughter lived locally and helped Violet with her shopping and cleaning the bungalow.

Violet's younger daughter is 63 years old and suffers with arthritis, so she can't manage to carry heavy bags of shopping. Violet would phone her daughter to tell her what she needed from the shop and her granddaughter would do an online shop once a week for all of them. However, as time went on, the slots for home delivery were extremely difficult to book.

People were having to take time off work because they either had the virus or had been in contact with someone who had the virus. This meant they had to self-isolate for ten days and could only return to work following a negative PCR (Polymerase chain reaction) test. People were being advised to take LFT (lateral flow test), which could be done at home. LFT tests were being given to anyone. You could get them from pharmacies, general practitioners, supermarkets, and libraries (most of which were Covid 19 testing centres and later vaccination hubs). Community centres were also being used as testing centres and vaccination hubs. Violet worried that her community centre may not open for her to enjoy the social interaction she once enjoyed.

Virologists world-wide were working tirelessly to produce a vaccine against the virus. On the 8th of December 2020, the first vaccine was given to a 91-year-old lady in England. At this time, hubs in the UK were starting to roll out vaccinating the over-80's and health care staff. Eventually, all adults would receive a double vaccination six months apart and then a further booster vaccine.

Violet and her family and friends were worried about having the vaccine but felt that they had no option. By this time, Violet had lost a few friends to Covid 19. Even though this was the case, Violet (against her daughter's advice) had decided not to be vaccinated.

Schools had been closed all around the world and the death rates were alarming. When Violet listened to the news, she became ever more anxious. The only people she had seen in months were her youngest daughter and granddaughter when they dropped off the shopping. She could tell her daughter was anxious about going out. They spoke through the window and Violet knew she was one of the lucky ones. Some of her friends didn't have family close by. She had heard of terrible predicaments where people in nursing homes couldn't see loved ones. She saw on the news that some nursing homes had made makeshift visiting booths so even though people couldn't touch each other, they could at least see one another. Violet felt more alone than she had ever been in her life.

Violet was scared and loneliness was a real issue now. She spent more time in bed, and her physical and mental health were deteriorating. She had been contacted by the practice nurse from her general practitioner's surgery. The nurse tried to encourage Violet to be vaccinated, explaining all the benefits and that soon, her friends would be able to get together and that she would be very vulnerable, and she wouldn't be able to go out and enjoy being with her friends again.

Violet understood but felt that the vaccine was so new she was frightened to have it. Her daughter got angry with her and said some awful things about never seeing her mother again and how some of Violet's friends had died before the vaccine had been developed. Violet not only felt lonely, she was now feeling bullied. She had times when she thought she would be better off dead. As time went on, her friends' phone calls became more infrequent. They didn't have any conversation because none of them were doing anything.

Loneliness and isolation have been a huge problem during the Covid 19 pandemic. Those requiring assistance to socialise were affected more than able-bodied people.

According to Age UK, there are 1.4 million older people in the UK who are often lonely, whereas Campaign To End Loneliness stated in 2021 that there are 9 million people in the UK and 4 million of these are older people.

Violet's granddaughter begged her grandmother to be vaccinated but Violet thought that the situation couldn't go on much longer. Then, variants of the virus were showing up. The first was called the Kent variant because that is where it was first discovered. Then the Delta variant was first discovered in India in late 2020. Then Omicron was detected in Botswana in South Africa in December 2021. This variant is highly contagious but fortunately it doesn't appear to be as severe.

Violet hasn't showered for days and is losing weight. Her daughter who was once really cross with her for not having the vaccine, is now extremely concerned that she is not taking care of herself. Doctor's appointments are difficult to access. Since the pandemic, everyone has to fill in an on-line assessment form. Violet's daughter tried to do this but without success. She eventually went to the surgery and spoke with the receptionist. She explained how concerned she was. The receptionist said she would email the doctor and that someone would visit Violet within a few days. When the doctor saw Violet, she was shocked. Her clothes were not only soiled they were hanging off her because of the amount of weight loss.

She asked Violet what had led to this deterioration and Violet broke down and cried. She explained that she didn't think the pandemic was so serious and that she didn't expect it to go on for so long.

The doctor listened to her concerns and asked her how she felt now about having the vaccine. Violet admitted she wished she had had the vaccine because she might as well be dead. She had been in isolation for so long that she was frightened to go outside. She had lost contact with so many friends and at times she had fallen out with her family. She asked the doctor if it was too late to have the vaccine?

Her reply was 'absolutely not.' Violet was relieved and asked how she could get it. The doctor also thought Violet would benefit from some antidepressants to help her adjust to the new world outside of her bungalow. Within a short space of time, Violet received the vaccine and was taking her new medication.

It took some time for her to adapt, but each day she felt a little stronger and gradually she felt brave enough to go for short walks with her daughter. She met some old friends and even went for lunch.

Violet realised just how much she had been missing out on. She was upset that the community centre was still being used as a testing centre, but she understood the importance of this. She hoped that she would live long enough to see the world and her little community return to normal.

Resources to help with loneliness and age-related problems:

www.ageuk.org/
www.redcross.org.uk/wellbeing – support line 10–6pm daily 0808 196 3651.

MAISY'S
STORY

DISORDERED EATING

Maisy is fifteen years old. She lives with her parents and her brother Luke who is twelve years old. Maisy has a small group of friends at school, and she enjoys playing netball. She plays netball for the county. She has played since she was eleven, when she first entered high school. Maisy isn't academic. She is pretty average in most of her subjects in school. Maisy's social life revolves around her netball. She travels every other weekend to play an opposing team. She gets on well with her coach and the other girls in the team. Life has been good for Maisy. She even gets along with her little brother.

When Maisy was away from home playing netball, she would take food that her mother had prepared for her. Her favourite was salad in a box with potato salad and some chocolate cake for dessert. Her mother always gave her extra bits, like crisps, nuts, or crackers. Maisy usually shared the extra bits with the girls. She very rarely brought anything home.

Maisy's thighs were getting a little chunky and comments were being made by the opposing teams. In particular, her net ball kit was getting tight, although this wasn't usually a problem as she was a growing girl, she felt that she hadn't grown up, so much as grown out and this was upsetting her.

Maisy had been the same size for over a year, so was very uncomfortable with this change.

She began to feel emotions that she had never experienced before. As time went on, she felt anxious about going into the changing rooms. Her shape had definitely changed over the past months, and she was self-conscious. She would try to hide from the other girls because she was embarrassed. All the girls were at different stages of puberty, but she thought her body was changing at a rate of knots. Her hips and breasts were filling out and she felt it was more noticeable on her than anyone else.

Maisy decided she couldn't carry on feeling like this. She decided she would take up running and cut out carbohydrates to see if she could increase her fitness and lose weight. She had made up her mind to take control because being overweight was making her feel miserable. Maisy told her parents, and they were pleased that she was mature enough to take responsibility for her own health and fitness.

Each morning, Maisy got up an hour earlier than usual to go for a run. She would shower and be ready for school before her mother was out of bed. Her parents thought it wouldn't last because Maisy was usually a nightmare to get out of bed in the morning. This routine became the norm for Maisy and very soon she was losing the weight. Her friends in school commented on how brilliant she looked. She was elated by all the comments. She was getting a buzz out of the exercise and so increased it.

She began to go to the gym in her school lunch break. There was always netball practice after school. She noticed that, because she wasn't carrying a few extra pounds, she was quicker and had more energy on the pitch. This also gave her a feeling of elation. She was happier than she'd been in a long time.

At weekends, when she wasn't playing netball, she would go to the shopping centre with the girls to spend her pocket money on makeup or treat herself to some costume jewellery or scrunchies for her hair. The girls enjoyed looking at clothes and whenever one of them had a birthday, they would go out for lunch. Life was good. Maisy enjoyed being with her friends.

Maisy's mother was the first to notice that Maisy was becoming a little underweight. She could see that her clothes were very loose. She also noticed that Maisy was putting most of her food in the bin. She spoke to Maisy about putting food in the bin and Maisy said, 'don't fuss Mum. I am fine. I get lots to eat in school.'

So, at first her mother thought she had better leave Maisy alone, after all, she had always been a very sensible young lady. Maisy was now noticing that her hair was falling out, so she bought some vitamins. She had always had very fine hair and this hair loss was a concern for her. She told herself that the vitamins would take time to work. She didn't for one minute think that her lack of nutrition could be causing her hair loss.

Several months had gone by since Maisy began to increase her exercise and reduce her calorie intake. Apart from the hair loss, Maisy noticed that her stamina had decreased. She was slowing down on her runs and on the netball pitch. The girls were shouting at her when she was playing. She noticed that she was dizzy on occasion. Maisy seemed to have this newfound determination to keep going even when she felt at times that she would pass out.

A couple of weeks later, Maisy realised that her periods had stopped. She wasn't too bothered as they were a nuisance to her, one she could live without. Maisy pushed and pushed herself. It was much harder to get up in the morning to go for her run. She found she was not running for as long as she used to. It wasn't giving her the buzz that she would usually get from it. By the time she had done her run, she had to rest before she could get in the shower.

Her closest friend was concerned enough to speak with Maisy's mother. Her mother explained that she had tried to talk to Maisy, but that Maisy had become a little snappy with her, so she thought she would just keep an eye on her. Maisy's friend said she was concerned because Maisy had confided in her about her periods stopping. Maisy's mother was shocked at this, so she said she would speak with her that evening. Maisy's friend said she would try to persuade her to join the other girls at lunch time instead of going to the gym.

Now very underweight and malnourished, it was obvious that Maisy had a problem. The school contacted Maisy's parents to express their concern. Maisy's mother asked her to come to the doctor with her, but Maisy was very defensive and said there wasn't a problem. Her family were getting frustrated and didn't know what to do. The school nurse gave them some resources to contact. Maisy's mother contacted Beat, which is a one-to-one web chat, help@beateatingdisorders.org.uk.

They were very helpful and gave lots of advice. They explained there was no quick fix, and that Maisy would need to realise that she had a problem. Once Maisy accepted her eating disorder, she would benefit from counselling. They also suggested that even if Maisy wasn't willing to go to the doctor, her mother should speak with them to enable them to understand the situation.

Maisy was going to need a lot of support from family, friends, and health professionals. Maisy's parents were devastated that they had encouraged her and thought she was doing the right thing at the beginning of this journey. Maisy felt as though suddenly her world was falling apart. She had a compulsion to continue with the vigorous exercise routine but no longer had the energy. One thing she didn't want to lose control of was her diet. She felt as though everyone was trying to shovel food into her.

She became angry and would snap at anyone who even mentioned food or the fact that she should put weight on. Maisy hadn't been weighed for months she didn't want to know what she weighed. She knew in her own mind that she needed to continue with her own eating regime, which she thought was healthy. She was under the illusion that she still needed to lose just a few pounds.

Hiding food was an everyday thing and she had become clever at devising ways of doing this. She would walk through the park on her way home from school and feed the ducks. She was no longer able to play netball but saw it as their loss because in her mind, she was still the fastest and most skilful in the team.

Her hair continued to fall out. Some of her teeth were wobbly. She'd decided there was no way she was telling anyone that. She was taking more and more time off school. She had very little energy and the joy had gone from her life. Everyone nagged her ALL the time to eat. Every day she battled with her parents who she felt were force feeding her, even though they were only trying to get her to drink some fortified drinks.

Life had gone full circle from her being at the top of her game in netball, to now being barely able to walk to the bathroom. At this point, Maisy's parents spoke yet again to her doctor and it was decided that against Maisy's will, she would have to be taken to hospital.

Maisy was emaciated. The doctors explained to her parents that she may not survive. They were devastated, left feeling guilty and responsible. Her whole family found it difficult to believe that their once beautiful, athletic daughter, was in a hospital bed looking like a skeleton. Some family members were supportive however, there were comments like 'how on earth didn't they do something before it got to this?' Others said, 'they should have taken her in and not allowed her to get into this state.' This made them feel even more guilt, at a time when she was literally at death's door.

Maisy underwent intensive treatment and after two months in hospital receiving nutrition, medication for depression and counselling, Maisy was able to return home. She was still extremely thin. Her parents were terrified that she would stop eating again and they might lose her.

Maisy continued with the counselling. She relapsed a few times but fortunately she was not admitted to hospital again. Maisy will never be able to relax around food. Everything she eats takes a conscious effort. Although in time, her health will improve, Maisy knows there is always that voice in her head telling her she's not good enough. The only way she felt in control and able to feel good about herself was when she was excessively exercising and eating virtually nothing. She will need support for the rest of her life.

Resources for disordered eating:

www.orri-uk.com/
www.betterhelp.com/
www.theeatingdisorderservice.com/
www.mind.org.uk

LEXI'S
STORY

BODY DYSMORPHIA

Lexi, a 42-year-old, began having Botox injections when she was in her twenties.

When the injections took effect, she noticed her skin was smoother. She felt fresher and felt that her makeup went on better. At first, she swore she wouldn't be one of those women who looked as though they were a rabbit caught in the headlights. Even though her friends were all having filler put in their lips, Lexi had always liked her lips. She had generous lips but after a while she too began to think she would look better with a little enhancement of her lips.

She went to several clinics to have her lips enhanced, but they turned her away. They told her she didn't need filler in her lips and anyone who did the procedure would be doing so unethically. As time went on, it played on her mind more and more. She became quite obsessive about it and looking back she feels that this was the turning point.

Because she struggled to find someone to make her lips bigger, she looked at herself in a different way. Whereas all her life she had liked the way her lips looked, now she thought they were thin and compared to friends who had had their lips enhanced, Lexi's were thinner.

Lexi eventually found someone to make her lips bigger. At first, she was shocked because they were massive, but in a few days when the swelling reduced, she was delighted with them. However, some of her friends told her they were way too big. From the side view, Lexi looked like she was permanently pouting.

Lexi continued having regular Botox and lip filler. As time went on, Lexi went for filler in her cheeks which she loved. Once again, she got the feeling of elation after the treatment. Still, she never quite felt satisfied with her overall appearance. Lexi was spending a lot of time and money having her acrylic nails done, her hair, and professional makeup each time she went out.

She then decided to consult a plastic surgeon to have her breasts enlarged. This was done a few weeks later. Her next procedure was a tummy tuck. By the time Lexi was thirty, she had undergone three breast augmentations, a tummy tuck, a rhinoplasty (nose job), an eye lift and liposuction.

Now at the age of 42 she was having more filler in her cheeks and lips. She was getting into a lot of debt to pay for these procedures. It seemed the more she had done, the more she felt she needed it. Her face was becoming distorted. Her lips were too large for her small face and the filler in her cheeks was lopsided.

Close friends and relatives were telling her to stop but she felt they were only jealous. Some of the aesthetic clinics she attended had banned her from making appointments. However, there is always some unscrupulous person who will not care because they just want your money. Lexi was never happy with the way she looked, and she was willing to travel abroad to have surgery. Her friends knew Lexi needed help. She was becoming grotesque, and they feared what she would do next.

Lexi was depressed when she was not undergoing some form of aesthetic procedure. She got a buzz from having treatments and when she wasn't, she became depressed. She was never satisfied with her appearance. She was beginning to become angry with the clinicians. She felt they weren't doing what she asked of them. Lexi felt that if she was paying, they should do whatever she asked them to do.

She began seeking advice from a medical claims' solicitor. She knew she was looking strange but thought the only way out of the situation was to have more surgery or treatments, and the only way to pay for more was to put a claim in for medical negligence.

She continued to have fillers and she developed an infection in her nasolabial fold (crease at the side of nose running down to the lip). The clinician who undertook this procedure was not insured and worse still, wasn't a medical professional. Unfortunately, her blood supply was restricted and the person who did it didn't recognise the signs.

It was a few days later when her skin turned black and became so painful that Lexi had to go to the accident and emergency department. She had to have the filler dissolved. This led to a nasty hole in her face and infection developing. Lexi was referred to a dermatologist who berated her for being so foolish for having the procedures. He told her of many women he had seen with similar problems. She had to undergo months of treatment before they could even consider plastic surgery.

It was at this point that Lexi was referred to a psychologist. She was more miserable than she had ever been. She struggled with money because she was paying off all the different clinics that she had had treatment from. She was spiralling downwards.

Lexi spent many years having treatment from the psychologist. She was given treatment from a hypnotherapist who used cognitive behavioural therapy. Lexi did stop having aesthetic procedures, but she not only had physical scars, she had mental scars that were taking much longer to heal. She continued with her battle in the courts, but the ruling was, because she had undergone all treatments after giving informed consent, she couldn't claim any compensation.

Lexi was in financial trouble because she now had massive bills for the solicitor and the courts. Her drive for perfection has led to her being insecure, anxious, depressed and physically and mentally scarred for life.

Lexi has a condition called body dysmorphia. In other words, she doesn't see herself as others see her and she is never happy with her appearance. She may be able to manage her disorder symptoms by changing the way she thinks and behaves.

Cognitive Behavioural Therapy (CBT) can help her to learn the triggers and teaches how to deal with her compulsion to undergo aesthetic procedures.

As with many psychological disorders, body dysmorphia begins slowly and the boost of endorphins that undergoing procedures gives the person, is the reason they continue to want more. They may also get a boost from the compliments received. Most people want to feel good about themselves and when they have aesthetic procedures, they can't recognise when they have had enough.

As a retired aesthetic practitioner there have been many occasions when I have refused treatments. If in my professional opinion, a procedure would not enhance someone's appearance, I would not undertake it.

People can become very aggressive when they don't get what they want. It was felt that my reputation as an excellent practitioner was important to me, and I wanted to uphold that reputation. You can imagine if a client has what I consider a false look about them, what people would say. Like many professions, you are only as good as your last client.

Medical practitioners take an oath to 'do no harm.' Therefore, I could never knowingly harm anyone.

Practicing aesthetic procedures was not something that ever sat comfortably with me. I enjoyed helping people to look their best, but I felt uncomfortable in myself. I prefer to offer advice on healthy eating, exercise and all aspects of self-love and care.

Resources for support with body dysmorphia:

www.betterhelp.com/
www.mind.org.uk

JAKE'S
STORY

WEIGHT LOSS

Jake, a 38-year-old married man, is obese and unfit. He wants to turn his life around and has joined slimming clubs on several occasions. He tends to lose weight quickly but then something in his life makes him give up.

For example, he was doing well with his eating and exercise regime, then his wife gave birth to their second child, and he felt he was unable to go out walking because he was leaving her alone with the babies. There was always some excuse, Jake had very little will power and loved food.

Unfortunately, he didn't enjoy cooking, so they ate a lot of takeaway food and convenience food.

His wife was overweight too but not as much as Jake. She was also still carrying a lot of baby weight.

Jake is 5'8", he weighs 18 stone. He went down to 12 stone at one point when he attended a slimming club. Jake knows exactly what he should be doing to maintain a healthy weight, but he is very weak willed. He has been to his doctor to ask for help. He hoped the doctor would refer him for a gastric band, but he told him he could go to a slimming club free of charge. The doctor wouldn't prescribe slimming tablets either.

Jake felt helpless and he was becoming more introverted. His job was sitting all day in a call centre, so he wasn't getting any exercise there. He usually called at the chip shop or pizza parlour on the way home. He knew his wife would appreciate that because she was tired after looking after the two little ones all day.

Jake had very little energy because of the extra weight he carried around and because he wasn't putting the right fuel in his body. Although he knew how much better he felt when he was slimmer, he just couldn't get motivated. There was always an excuse to eat chocolate or some other treat he thought he deserved. The treat gave him a short-lived boost.

Jake's family were all overweight, but none were as big as Jake. His mother was concerned for his health. Jake's father died of a heart attack when he was 46, so his mother knew Jake was putting himself at risk. There were other hereditary health conditions that Jake was at risk of developing.

His mother and sister had type 2 diabetes. His mother also had high cholesterol and high blood pressure. All of these health conditions can be brought about by being overweight.

Jake took a lot of time off work. He always had a cold or back ache or stomach problems. He swung from having diarrhoea to constipation. Jake knows how much better he feels when he follows a healthy diet, but he is lazy and has no motivation. However, Jake was in for a rude awakening when he found out he too had high blood pressure, high cholesterol, and type 2 diabetes. This was Jake's wake up call. He decided to go back to the slimming club and to start walking again. He couldn't bear the thought of going to a gym or swimming (which would have been the best form of exercise) because he felt so ashamed of his size.

Swimming is the best form of exercise for overweight people because it is non-weightbearing. Jake decided to walk for a short time, several times a day. He found this to be difficult at first, especially as the new beta blockers he had been prescribed were slowing him down. His diabetes was being treated by diet alone and his high cholesterol was being treated by diet and statins.

He was told he could come off all medication if he kept his BMI (body mass index) within normal limits. Jake lost weight quickly at first, which gave him the encouragement to continue. The benefits outweighed the ease of slipping into old habits of eating junk food.

The problem was, Jake had been here before and had relapsed on several occasions.

Yo-yo dieting is very harmful - it can cause fatty liver, high blood pressure, diabetes, and heart disease. It also increases body fat percentage at the expense of muscle mass and strength.

As we can see, this could have already impacted on Jake's health. Changing eating habits for life is not going on a diet, it is a healthy eating regime. This needs to be adopted for Jake to be successful.

He decides to visit a hypnotherapist to keep him on track. Jake's life begins to improve. He doesn't have any food in his house that isn't good for him. He has also seen a big improvement in his wife and consequently, his sex life. He knows that he is setting the scene for a healthy lifestyle for his children.

Jake is more determined than ever to make it work this time. He even finds a new job, something he never thought he would do. His new job as a post man will ensure he walks several miles a day. Being out in the fresh air has improved his mental health and he no longer dreads exercising. He goes swimming with the children and can kick a ball around in the park. Jake is so much happier than he has ever been. Jake enjoyed renewing his wardrobe and was taking much more care of himself in every way. He is determined to stay on track and is taking pride in his appearance.

He realises his poor eating habits began when he was young. He had a sweet tooth and was always eating biscuits, crisps, and chocolate. He also remembers his mother giving him food as a treat for being good or as a reward for doing well in school. He now knows not to do this with his children. He rewards with days out in nature or a board game the whole family can play. He is determined now that he has children, to continue this healthy way of life.

Resources to help with weight loss:

www.thinkingslimmer.com/nhs
www.betterme-meal-plan.com/nhs
www.weightwatchers.com/uk/
www.slimmingworld.co.uk

SAM'S
STORY

SAFE SEX

Sam, a 54-year-old single man has contracted a sexually transmitted disease. He is homosexual and has had several partners. Sam doesn't practice safe sex and he knows he has passed the infection to others.

Sam is a foolish, selfish man. He doesn't care that he has made others poorly. His philosophy is that he got it from someone, so why should he care? He is attending a genitourinary medicine (GUM) Clinic. He has been diagnosed with gonorrhoea. It's not the first time he has had this disease and because of his lack of care and compassion for others, it probably won't be his last. He has also contracted other sexually transmitted diseases. He has received treatment from the GUM clinic successfully before. They constantly offer advice regarding practicing safe sex, but Sam is blasé about his sexual health.

Sam knows he should use a condom to protect himself and his partner, but he doesn't like using them and is prepared to take the risk. Sam uses an app to find men who want casual sex. With a few clicks, Sam can find a sexual partner. When he has sex with a random man, it's usually following a night out, having taken drugs, alcohol, or both. This lowers his ability to make good decisions and can lead to risky behaviours like unprotected sex.

In general, Sam drinks too much alcohol. He smokes and doesn't eat a healthy diet. He chooses values in different areas: for example, he thinks nothing of spending money on his appearance. He wears designer clothes; his hair is always kept neat and tidy. He is slim, but he eats very little in the way of nutrition. He eats takeaway and ready meals and very rarely cooks for himself. He neglects himself in some areas but thinks he takes care of himself because he looks good.

Sam uses the dating apps to find sexual partners. Although he would like to find a man who would be his companion, he has had several failed relationships and feels it isn't worth it anymore at his age. So, he uses them for casual sex. He finds that these encounters give him instant gratification and they take away the sadness in his life for a short time.

Following the temporary emotional relief, he is left feeling guilty, more anxious, isolated, and even more depressed. According to Jack Turban, a physician and medical writer at Harvard Medical School, since 2007, more gay men have died from suicide than from HIV. This implies they are desperately searching for happiness. From the research undertaken by Jack

Turban, dating apps are contributing to mental health problems in the gay community.

Sam's self-esteem is very low, but he puts on a façade to the outside world. Sam is an angry man who has struggled to be accepted within his family and society. He has little love for himself and others. This may stem from being made to feel like an outcast from an early age. He has struggled all his life to fit in and now has little regard for himself and others. He is a well-known character in and around the clubs he frequents. Everybody chats to him, and he loves being the centre of attention. His flamboyance is renowned. He craves attention which he readily receives. But when he goes home and is on his own, he is desperately lonely and miserable. His life is like a seesaw going from the elation he feels when he is in the limelight, to the depths of despair when he is on his own.

Sam could seek support and help from **mindout.org.uk** or **lgbt.foundation**, amongst many other websites and local support groups.

However, the issue is whether or not Sam realises or accepts he has a problem. To him, it's just a way of life. It's normal to feel rejected, anxious, and angry all of the time. It is his behaviour towards others and his lack of self-esteem that will inevitably exacerbate his problems. Maybe if Sam had been born in a different generation that is more accepting of his sexual orientation, his mental and therefore physical health may not be so much of a problem.

Resources for gay men:

www.stonewall.org.uk
www.LGBT.foundation.uk

KATE'S
STORY

PRESCRIPTION MEDICATION

Kate is 36 years old. She works as a nursey nurse. When she was 29 years of age, she was in a skiing accident. She broke her left arm and her left femur. She was off work for six months and had a slow return to work because she needed physiotherapy.

Kate is the type of person who just gets on with things and she hated being immobile and dependent on others. To enable Kate to recover quickly, she took a cocktail of prescribed medication. She found it difficult to sleep initially after the accident, so took diazepam. This drug is very helpful short term but can become addictive. It is a central nervous system depressant. It also helps with anxiety.

Kate was prescribed co-codamol which is an analgesia. The dose was 30mg codeine and 500mg paracetamol. This may also be addictive if taken for long periods. To reduce inflammation, Kate was prescribed Voltarol suppositories - 100mg, once a night. Voltarol is a non-steroidal anti-inflammatory containing diclofenac sodium.

Kate found she was unable to wean herself off these drugs as easily as she had anticipated. She was experiencing side effects such as constipation, and reduced appetite. She noticed her coordination was impaired. When she tried to reduce the amount of analgesia she was taking, she was in considerable pain and there was no way she could do the exercises the physiotherapist had prescribed for her.

The longer time went on, her doctor was reluctant to prescribe some of her medication. Her doctor had a chat and explained that she needed to reduce the number of drugs she was taking. The doctor was very clear and explained to Kate how long-term use can damage the kidneys and the liver.

Kate agreed and the doctor stopped the diazepam and the Voltarol. It was decided that in order for Kate to continue with physiotherapy, the co-codamol was continued. A review was agreed in one month.

It was shortly after these drugs were discontinued that Kate found she couldn't sleep. She tried many natural remedies, but nothing worked. She was frustrated and each day was getting worse. She was irritable through lack of sleep. She was due to return to work soon and she became anxious that she wouldn't be able to cope.

Kate began taking over the counter Nytol to help her sleep, but this didn't work, even though she doubled the recommended dose. She told her friend that she was at her wits end and was desperate for a night's sleep. Her friend offered her a few diazepam and said to take one every other night to try and get her into a routine.

Kate found that on the nights she took the diazepam, she had a great sleep. So, she went back to her doctor who gave her a reduced dose. Kate started off by taking double the dose but was able to reduce it slowly. At last, she felt half human again. Although her doctor did tell her that this prescription was a one off and she had to adjust to sleeping without it. Her GP recommended relaxation therapies and gentle yoga to help with suppleness.

Her review was looming for the co-codamol, and Kate became increasingly worried about this.

Kate was doing really well with her physiotherapy and started a return to work. She was only working three mornings a week to begin with, and she found she had really missed her work colleagues and the children. Her concentration was poor and if she had had a bad night the night before, she found her patience with the children wasn't what it used to be.

Kate went for her review regarding the co-codamol. She was told she should be ready to drop down to taking paracetamol. Although she knew this was coming, she was very anxious about it. Kate did as she was told and stopped the co-codamol. She commenced taking paracetamol four times a day. Kate found herself desperate for some good sleep and on top of this, she began to feel depressed. She still had pain in her leg but felt that if she had a good sleep, she would be able to cope with this.

She was very moody and irritable. Her colleagues noticed a big change in her and they were worried about her. Kate knew she couldn't go on like this, so she looked at other ways to procure the drugs she needed. The friend who had given her the diazepam became a constant supply for Kate.

Kate felt extremely guilty, but she asked her grandmother to give her some of her Zapain (which is the same as co-codamol). Her grandmother had no idea that Kate was now dealing with addiction. She happily supplied Kate because she thought it was terrible that Kate was in pain. Kate also had a neighbour who said she had lots of Zapain left over from an old knee injury. Kate was building up a stock now and felt that if she had enough to last a few months, she could slowly wean herself off them. Unfortunately, rather than reducing the amount she was taking, Kate realised she needed more and more to make her feel better.

Kate was struggling with her addiction; she didn't know which way to turn. She thought she could handle it herself but, in her heart, she knew it was out of hand.

The big decision was made for Kate when her grandmother had a word with her mother (who was oblivious to the extended drug taking). Kate's mother had a heart to heart with her. She told her the truth about herself, which was very difficult for Kate to hear. Her mother explained that Kate had lost weight, she sometimes looked unkempt, her skin was sallow, she was moody and spoke to people with little respect. Her mother said 'I want my daughter back. I feel like I am losing you. What can I do to help?'

Kate broke down and explained how she thought she could deal with it. She told her mother she never anticipated this all those months ago when she had the accident. Her mother responded by telling Kate how proud everyone was by her remarkable recovery, but that they didn't know she was still struggling. Kate promised to go back to the doctor and ask for help. Her mother told her that she must be honest about all the medication she had been taking, apart from what has been prescribed. Kate promised she would.

Kate saw a different doctor who was very sympathetic. She was referred for rehabilitation. Kate was given counselling and help to reduce the drugs she was taking. She was put on a detox programme, which is the process by which all traces of harmful substances are removed from the body. Kate was given more time off work to recuperate. She found it difficult and suffered terrible withdrawal symptoms. But she knew she wanted to get back to her old self, so she continued, even when she had muscle pain, sweating, agitation, insomnia, and nausea.

Detoxification should never be tried without medical help and should be the first phase of recovery. Kate is going to need counselling, medication, nutritional advice, and an aftercare programme. This is not a quick fix, and the aftercare programme can help maintain long-term sobriety.

Kate thought she would be the last person to be going through this. Had it not been for support from friends and family, she may not have received the help she needed. Kate was always a strong healthy person in both mind and body, so she slipped into the addiction without realising. She knows she would behave differently if faced with her accident in the future. She took the medication thinking she would recover more quickly but didn't realise the damage she was doing. Kate has some minor damage to her liver but it's the psychological damage that will be the hardest for Kate in the long term.

<u>Resources for prescription medication addiction:</u>

www.priorygroup.com
www.mayoclinic.org

SHAUN'S
STORY

ALCOHOLISM

Shaun is 48 years old. He is an alcoholic.

He is a Chief Executive Officer (CEO) in a big company. He leads a team of executives to consider major decisions within the company. Over the years, Shaun has travelled the world with his job and enjoying the company of other CEOs is part of his social life. They are all highfliers with ambition. Shaun has always enjoyed a drink, but his drinking has become a concern for his wife.

They have four young children. Shaun works hard so when his wife shows concern about his drinking, he becomes aggressive. He tells her he needs a drink to unwind and that he doesn't have a problem. She understands he works hard but the drinking is happening more and more. She knows Shaun can't go a day without having a drink.

She is worried for the children because recently, the police were called by someone walking their dog in the local park. Shaun had gone out with the oldest two children, and he was sat on a bench while they played on the playground. The man walking his dog noticed it was getting dark and the children were quite young.

He approached Shaun to ask if everything was alright? Shaun was angry and told him to mind his own business. The smell of alcohol was overwhelming but when the children came over and complained of being hungry, the stranger became more concerned. He said, "you should get the children home."

At this point, Shaun got really aggressive, and the man rang the police as he walked away to inform them of the incident. The police arrived and took Shaun and the children home. Shaun's wife had been out of her mind with worry. He had forgotten his phone and she didn't know where he had gone. She thanked the police. They informed her they would have to contact social services.

Jane (Shaun's wife) felt that this was the last straw. She told Shaun if he didn't go to a rehabilitation clinic, she would leave him. Shaun knew he had to do something about his drink problem.

Shaun admitted himself into a clinic. He is fortunate enough to be able to afford this. He underwent therapy to help him detox. This was in the form of medication to reduce the cravings, and talking therapies. Shaun was ashamed of how the addiction had become so bad that he almost lost his family. He had been in denial for years and only now did he realise he had a problem.

Through the talking therapies, he realised just how bad things had become. He was making poor decisions in work, he had lost friends, his wife had endured countless episodes of his mood swings and aggressive behaviour - she knew the routine now; he would behave badly and then come home with expensive gifts or holidays that she would have to cancel. She couldn't risk taking the children on holiday with him because she wouldn't have her family or friends to support her when he kicked off.

The most upsetting for him was that he had put his children in danger several times. Jane had had to take his car keys off him, she had had to take the children to her mother for their safety. Shaun had fallen out with his in-laws, whom he had previously found to be good company and supportive in their marriage. He had broken promises over and over to get help. He was becoming physically sick from the alcohol abuse.

He was always proud of his physique but over the past few years, his muscles became flabby. He had a paunch and because of the damage to his liver, his skin was yellowing. He had lost his libido. He constantly suffered from colds or stomach upsets because his immune system was weakened. He never had a good night's sleep, so this made him irritable and unable to concentrate.

Shaun had a long recovery ahead of him. Alcohol had taken its toll on his mental health too. He didn't have the same concentration. He suffered some memory loss, and the anxiety was becoming unbearable. He was putting his addiction before everything. His family and work colleagues had had enough, he needed to be prepared to get help. Because he had admitted himself into the clinic, everyone rallied round to support him and his family.

What started as a few drinks to relax and take the stress of the day away, had become an addiction out of control. The drinking increased over time and wasn't seen as a problem until it impacted every aspect of his life.

Resources for those suffering with alcoholic addiction:

www.alcoholchange.org.uk
www.mind.org.uk
www.drinkaware.co.uk

LUCY'S
STORY

SELF-HARM

When Lucy was twelve years old, her father died. Lucy is an only child. Her father was her rock. Ben (Lucy's father) had taken care of her shortly after she was born. Her mother had what was thought at the time to be post-natal depression. However, this turned out to be a mental health condition that had gone undiagnosed for many years and was exacerbated by the birth of Lucy.

Lucy's mother was bi-polar, so she swung from being ecstatic to low in mood. Ben worked full time as a butcher so as much as it broke his heart, Lucy went to nursery full time when she was six months old. Ben was a quiet, patient man who had a caring nature. They lived in a high-rise block, which made them feel fairly isolated. They knew the neighbours on the same landing. The lady next door was elderly, so Ben often did her shopping. The other neighbours barley said hello and Ben was glad because he had his suspicions that they were drug users and there were always empty bottles and cans left lying around.

He saw the same rough looking people hanging around and he avoided them like the plague. He had tried to get a house exchange but was told that with only one child, he had no chance. People with four little ones were a priority. He understood this, so just kept his head down. Being an only child meant that Lucy was lonely. Ben would try to get her out in the fresh air as often as he could. He would take her to the local park or the beach. She loved the beach most of all. They would collect shells and decorate sandcastles with them. Lucy was very close to her father, and they shared the same sense of humour. As Lucy grew, her father taught her things that under normal circumstances, her mother would have taught her.

Lucy came home from school one day and was shocked to find the police in her flat. She had seen the police car outside her block of flats but didn't think anything of it because it was a regular occurrence. But when she saw the police officers in her flat and her mother distraught, she was terrified.

The police officer asked Lucy her name and how old she was. All she could say was, "why are you here?" The police officer said, "Please sit down, I am so sorry, but we have some sad news." Lucy's heart was racing. It pounded like a million drums that made her chest hurt - it seemed to make everything echo. She felt that she was spinning out of control. She didn't want to know what the sad news was. She wanted to go back down in the smelly lift and for them to go away.

The officer was talking but Lucy couldn't hear what she was saying. It was as though her head was in a bucket of water. **Blah blah blah** and I am sure you and your mum will be fine. You will be able to support each other and **blah blah blah** again. "What are you saying," Lucy shouted.

"Don't speak so quickly, I can't understand you."

"Ok love, you are bound to be shocked. Do you want to let your mum explain everything to you?" Lucy was totally bemused; she couldn't grasp what was being said. The police left the flat after making a cup of tea for the pair. Her mother was crying, and Lucy was struggling to get any sense out of her.

"Please Mum, calm down, Just, tell me what has happened. Dad will be home soon."

"No, he won't, he's never coming home again." Then there was lots of sobbing. Eventually, through snot and tears, Lucy was told that her father had been hit by a car outside of the butchers where he worked. He had been pronounced dead at the scene.

Her mother was never very reliable because she had mental health problems and Lucy felt that she had to take care of her mother now. Her mother took medication which did help, but she wasn't always great in taking her medication. Following the death of her father, Lucy spent most of her time in her room, listening to music, playing computer games, and reading. Lucy's only escape was school, and she wasn't happy there. She found it difficult to make friends and didn't join in any after school activities. She was becoming more of an introvert and was finding it difficult to communicate with other family members. Her grandparents put it down to her grieving and going through puberty. All of which were true, but there were other more worrying signs that her family may have picked up on, had they realised that Lucy was in a very dark place.

Lucy's self-esteem was lower than ever because her school uniform didn't get washed unless she did it herself. She often came home from school and had to go shopping for food and then prepare dinner. Lucy was tired all the time because her nutrition was so poor, and she didn't get good quality sleep. Losing a parent at a young age is always extremely upsetting, but when that person means everything to you, it can be devastating.

The first time Lucy self-harmed was when she had to join in with sports day. She was terrified of her classmates ridiculing her for not having the correct kit. She was also underdeveloped for her age and made every excuse to get out of doing PE. In order to get out of doing sports day she hit her ankle with a rock from the garden. It bruised and swelled overnight, and Lucy was elated in school the next day when she showed her teacher. Her plan had worked beautifully. Lucy had found such a relief from getting out of doing sports day that on reflection, she realises her self-harming probably stemmed from this act.

When she was alone in her room, she found a release of tension that had built up over the day by cutting her forearm, ever so slightly at first. Yes, it was painful, but the pain was a distraction from the awful pain she felt inside.

Her self-loathing was gaining momentum and she took time off school when her arms were sore. Rubbing her arms when they had started to heal was another way that Lucy could self-harm when she was around people. They would have no idea what she was doing. As Lucy did all her own washing, the fact that her clothes were blood-stained wasn't picked up. The self-harm continued for over a year, unnoticed by anyone. Lucy was very accomplished at hiding her secret. Until one day in school her classmate said, "you are bleeding."

Lucy made an excuse, but the other girl told the teacher and Lucy was asked to stay behind after class.

Lucy was terrified, her heart pounding in her chest as she sat and waited for the classroom to empty. The girls in her class were looking at her as they passed her desk. She knew it would be all over the school by tomorrow.

Mrs Simpson (Lucy's teacher) was quietly spoken, and she asked Lucy if she was ok. Lucy replied, "yes I am fine, I need to get home, my Mum needs me." Mrs Simpson could see Lucy was very anxious and she was rubbing her arms. Mrs Simpson told Lucy that she could go home soon but she just wanted a few minutes to chat. Lucy became distressed and started to cry. Mrs Simpson told her that everything would be alright and that she had noticed Lucy struggling for a while.

Mrs Simpson said, "you need support Lucy. You've taken on too much for a long time. There are plenty of people who can help you. I will refer you to Child and Adolescent Mental Health Services - CAMHS. We also have pastoral support in school. Now that we know you are suffering, we can help you." Lucy didn't know whether to be relieved or angry. Her feelings where like a roller coaster at that moment. She felt like she was spiralling out of control.

It's difficult to measure how many people self-harm because not everyone is picked up. There are many ways of self-harming, and some may not be considered 'self-harm.' Boys are more likely to punch a wall to relieve pressure. This isn't always recognised as self-harm.

There are many reasons why people self-harm: -

- Expressing or coping with emotional distress.
- Trying to feel in control.
- Punishing themselves.
- Relieving unbearable tension.
- A cry for help.
- A response to intrusive thoughts.

Here are some examples of what causes them to self-harm:

- Being bullied.
- Under pressure.
- Family problems.
- Money worries.
- Low self-esteem.
- Stress, anxiety, or depression.
- Confusion about sexuality.
- Grief.

- Physical or sexual abuse.
- Mental health issues.

Lucy will receive help now that her problems are out in the open.

Some of the coping strategies Lucy has been given are listed below: (I have included some helpful resources.)

- Hit a cushion.
- Talk to someone or call a help line.
- Do a hobby you enjoy.
- Listen to loud music.
- Take a shower.
- Do some exercise.
- Go for a walk.
- Focus on breathing.
- Wrap yourself in a duvet.
- Rip up a newspaper.
- Write down how you feel.

Find a strategy that works for you. Any distraction will help. Most importantly, **tell someone how you feel**.

<u>Resources for self-harming adolescents:</u>

NHS under 19, call ChildLine **- 0800 1111**
MIND, call **- 0300 123 33 93**
Young minds Parents Helpline, open 9.30 – 4pm **–
0808 802 5544**

DANIEL'S
STORY

SUICIDE

Waking that morning was the saddest thing to ever happen to Daniel. His mind was foggy, but he could still remember some of what had happened the night before. He desperately didn't want to be alive this morning. He absolutely didn't want to hear those words from a care worker!

'Back in the land of the living, are we?' The noise of the trolleys up and down the corridor was as if someone was scratching the inside of his brain. He wanted the solace of the blackness he had sunk so readily into the night before. He pulled the blanket over his head to try desperately to get away from the world. Daniel lay in the hospital bed and sobbed. He sobbed so hard his body shook. A nurse popped her head around his door and decided to leave him a little longer before disturbing him.

Daniel was in despair; he couldn't carry on living with the burdens he carried. He had (as far as he was concerned) the most miserable life. Every day he had to push himself just to get out of bed. He knew he had to because he had people relying on him. He felt if he wasn't there, they would have to get on without him.

He didn't think of the devastation he would leave behind.

Thinking beyond his own sadness was beyond his reach right now. Consumed by the heaviness and the black cloud looming over him, he simply could not carry on. He knew how he would do it. Waiting until he would be on his own. The night he tried to take his own life, he had made sure his wife and son were staying at a friend's house. He had a stash of tablets and a bottle of alcohol. He thought if he did it quickly, the cocktail he was about to take wouldn't kick in before he had chance to take it all. The last thing he wanted was to do a half-hearted job. It was as though he was in a daze when he took the first handful of tablets, washed down with a glass of vodka. This soon followed with another and another. He was surprised that it was taking a while for the effects to kick in.

He was watching some mind-numbing quiz show when the effects began to take hold, and the nausea and the dizziness took over. He hoped he wouldn't vomit and have to start again. He was desperate for the pain to go away. That's when the sleepy all-consuming wooziness fell on him like a weighted blanket. He embraced this feeling and sunk down and down until there were no more thoughts, no more worries popping unwanted into his brain.

Daniel was married to a quiet woman who didn't work because they had a disabled little boy. Daniel's family were unable to support him because they too had health problems. His in-laws lived in France so were also unable to offer support. Daniel had been made redundant several years ago and he had only been able to secure jobs that were low paid, and he hated going to work. He resented his boring life that offered no joy. He couldn't remember the last time he laughed or even felt happy.

His life was a round of pushing himself to get out of bed, going to a job he hated, leaving his wife to cope with their disabled son. His friends weren't really friends, more like acquaintances. He was in a financial mess because of borrowing over the years. Even his redundancy money didn't help for long.

Every aspect of his life seemed bleak. Because he was in such a dark place, he had forgotten how much he loved his wife and son. He had forgotten how lucky he was to be able to work and with his qualifications and experience, he could keep trying to get a better job. He had given up going out with friends, so they had stopped asking. However, they were still there, just felt unwanted. Daniel only had to reach out.

Waking up in this sterile room may not have been what Daniel wanted but it was what he had. His head pounded like a million drums. The light hurt his eyes. His throat was raw. The nurse came back in the room and softly asked if he wanted a drink of water. She helped him; his hands shook like he was mixing a cocktail. He had no control over it. The light hurt his eyes. She could see it was bothering him, so she turned the light off and part drew the curtains. She explained how he would be seeing the doctor soon and he would have a referral to a psychiatrist.

Daniel asked if his wife knew where he was. The nurse said yes. He told her he didn't want to see anyone. She understood and said that it was his choice.

Kerry (Daniels wife) was devastated when she heard that he had tried to take his own life. She was also very angry with him – 'how dare he leave her with their severely disabled son,' she thought. Kerry took the vast responsibility for their son, so she found it difficult to understand why he felt desperate enough to go to these lengths. Daniel hadn't disclosed the financial difficulties they were in. She knew he wasn't happy, but they were both struggling. He was supposed to be her rock.

The shock of hearing that he was serious about taking his life left her feeling so many different emotions. She wanted to see him but didn't know how she would react. Frightened of showing anger, she thought it was prudent to wait until she could process what had happened. Yet, how could she not want to see her husband when he needed her most? Questions flew around in her brain, but the main question was why? Why would he be so selfish? She went from being sorry for him, to being angry, then so hurt and upset that she had almost lost him.

Kerry's friend told her she could stay a little while longer until she felt strong enough to cope at home. Relieved and grateful, Kerry decided to pick up some more clothes for herself and her and son go to the hospital the following day. Her friend was well placed to offer advice because she worked as a child social worker. She told Kerry she would make enquiries about her son going to day care until he was old enough to go to school. It was hoped that this would lift some of the burden from the couple.

Daniel was in the system now and albeit a long road to recovery, he was at least on that road. Daniel will need a lot of support and therapy. He was now part of a dreadful statistic. The suicide rate for men in England and Wales in 2019 was the highest for two decades, data from the Office for National statistics found there were 5,691 suicides registered, with an average standardised rate of 11 deaths per 100,000 population. **Men accounted for about three**

quarters of registered suicides in 2019, 4,303 compared with 1,388 women.

Men are less likely to admit when they feel vulnerable. Women seek help earlier. Young boys are conditioned not to show feelings whereas girls are allowed to show emotions. Men tend to try and sort out their problems by themselves. This can however be through destructive behaviour such as alcohol or drug abuse. These strategies are often the reason men become more profoundly depressed and behaviours become more impulsive. There are many resources to help both men and women when they are in need of support.

Resources for men in need of support:

Campaign Against Living Miserably (CALM) - **www.thecalmzone.net**
Samaritans are available 24/7: call **116 123**
Mind information, call - **0300 123 3393: www.mind.org.uk**
You can also contact your own general practitioner.

KENNY'S
STORY

PROSTATE CANCER

Kenny was waking several times during the night to go to the toilet. When he went to urinate, he took a while to get started and felt as though he were forcing himself to go. He was going out of the house much less and always had to make sure there was a toilet nearby because he needed to go much more often. He was sure it was part of the aging process and Elsie (his wife) thought the same. She had several age-related health problems, so they joked about it being better than the alternative. They were both in their late sixties and Elsie chatted to her friends about the trials and tribulations of age.

Kenny and Elsie have three children, Steve who is forty-five, Kevin - forty-three, and Rob - forty-one. Kenny has a great relationship with his sons, but he is a very private man and never discusses health issues with anyone. He even gets embarrassed talking to Elsie about it. They only broach the subject if Elsie brings it up. Although she thinks it's nothing serious, she is concerned for Kenny so she has asked him several times to go to the doctor. She thinks they may be able to prescribe a tablet to help.

The boys have noticed for some time that when they take Dad for a pint, he goes to the toilet approximately every twenty minutes. They discussed it amongst themselves but just like Dad, they find it very difficult to broach the subject. Rob is married to a nurse, so he mentioned to the other two that he would get her opinion on Dad's health. When Rob told his wife how they were concerned, she said "there is probably nothing to worry too much about. These symptoms can be an enlarged prostate, but it needs to be checked out because he shouldn't be suffering like this and there are treatments for enlarged prostate. Should it be anything more sinister, then **it's better to get checked out as soon as possible**."

Rob did some research and next time he saw his brothers, he told them what his wife had said and about what he has discovered. They agreed Dad should get checked out. The difficult part would be how they approach him.

Eventually, they thought it best to speak with Mum as she was more approachable. Next time they were all together was several weeks from when they had said they were going to speak to Mum. Rob's wife was there to offer support. Elsie knew the boys were right, but she told them, "I have been trying for months to get him to see the doctor." They had no idea that Mum and Dad had even noticed there was a problem. They were relieved in one way that at least there was acknowledgement of a health concern. However, they hadn't realised how long it had been going on for and that poor Dad was exhausted from lack of sleep.

Rob's wife tried to put their minds at rest and without making them too anxious, she wanted to impress how serious this could be. Elsie promised she would speak with Kenny that evening.

The next day, Kenny made an appointment with his doctor. He was nervous about the appointment as he was convinced the examination would involve a digital rectal examination. He didn't know if he preferred a male or female. He was extremely embarrassed at just the mere thought of it. Elsie told him she would come along to the surgery with him for moral support.

The doctor was male, and he felt relieved. He explained his symptoms and how long he had been experiencing them. The doctor was understanding but told Kenny he should never have put off coming to see him for so long. In fact, Kenny had been suffering for years. The doctor explained how the prostate worked and exactly where it was situated. He told Kenny that he was right to some extent that the prostate does become enlarged with age but that if you are waking several times to pee in the night, then it's time to do something about it.

He went on to say, these symptoms are not always a sign of cancer however they most definitely need to be checked out. He explained that **any health problem is easier to treat if caught early**. He explained that he would take a blood sample called a prostate specific antigen (PSA). The doctor could tell Kenny was nervous so he said he would see him in one week for the results of the blood test and that at that time, he would undergo a digital rectal examination. He wanted to build a bit of rapport with Kenny.

One week later he was back at the surgery. The blood results were of concern and the doctor was very reassuring when he explained that Kenny would need to have biopsies and an MRI (magnetic resonance imaging) scan.

The digital rectal examination was over very quickly, and Kenny was made to feel at ease. He joked with the doctor as his way of managing his embarrassment.

He said, "if you find anything worth having up there, you can keep it." The doctor was used to men being embarrassed so kept the banter going.

Elsie told the boys about their dad's appointment, and they were relieved that he was having tests. They were also concerned about the blood results.

Two weeks later, Kenny had an MRI scan. This showed that he had cancer. Radiographers use a score called the Likert score; it tells your doctor how likely you are to have cancer. The score is between 1-5 and Kenny's was 5 which meant he very likely has cancer and would need to go on to have biopsies taken. The biopsies were positive too.

The family were devastated. Kenny put on a brave face, but he was terrified. He began his treatment at the hospital which went on for over a year.

Elsie was desperate to help so she found some anecdotal evidence to show that eating cruciferous vegetables such as broccoli, brussels sprouts and kale may help. She also found Lycopene found in tomatoes was supposed to be beneficial.

Apparently, there is more lycopene in cooked tomatoes than raw.

Rob's wife was also on board with the healthy eating plan, so she did some research and found these foods to be of benefit:-

- Fish
- Soy
- Omega 3 fatty acids.
- Green tea
- Vit E
- Vit C

She also found it is best to avoid diets high in calcium, trans fatty acids (found in margarines), fried and baked food, because they may stimulate prostate cancer growth. Animal fats are also thought to be unhealthy so should be avoided. She found this information from **www.healthline.com.**

Kenny realises he should have attended screening and because he was embarrassed, he put off going to the doctor for a very long time. He has made it abundantly clear to his sons that no matter how embarrassed they are, they must attend screening, especially with the family history. Kenny will never know if he could have avoided getting cancer, but he knows he would have a better chance of survival if he had sought help sooner. Prostate cancer doesn't always have any symptoms early on, so screening is vital to save lives.

Resources for support with prostate cancer:

www.cancerresearchuk.org
www.prostatecanceruk.org

DYLAN'S
STORY

ANABOLIC STEROID ABUSE

Dylan is small in stature at 5'7". He has always been self-conscious regarding his height. He became a member of his local gym when he was twenty years old. He paid for a year subscription because he thought it would encourage him keep going. Very enthusiastic at first, he went every night after work. This waned to three times a week which he found more sustainable.

Dylan was a jovial, confident type, who had a small group of friends. His best mate Jake joined the gym shortly after Dylan and they soon got into a routine of going three nights a week together. They would encourage each other by seeing who could do the most sit-ups and bench presses etc. Jake being 6'1" and a stockier build than Dylan, always had the edge. At first, they used to laugh about it, but Dylan's self-consciousness meant the longer this went, on the more it bothered him.

When they went to the pub with their other mates, Jake would inevitably bring up the subject of how much iron he could pump. He enjoyed showing off but tried not to embarrass Dylan. However, the other lads would ask Dylan how he was doing and when he wouldn't answer or tried to change the subject, they would skit at him. Dylan laughed with them but deep down, it hurt him. He thought about giving up going to the gym even though he could see an improvement in his physique. It was slow progress and Dylan became impatient. He'd become friendly with a few people at the gym and explained to a guy who was very well built that he was getting frustrated because he had been going to the gym for about eight months and his physique had improved, but not to the extent that he wanted. The guy said he used a pill to give himself a boost. Dylan thought he meant vitamins or protein pills, so he decided he would start taking some.

The protein drinks were nice and came in lots of different flavours. Dylan was taking far too many (which can damage your kidneys). He kept this up for a further three months but saw little improvement. He told the guy at the gym who laughed and said, "I thought you knew what I was talking about but had decided it wasn't for you."

Dylan listened while this guy explained that he knew where to get anabolic steroids. Dylan was dubious but thought if he took them for a short while until he had the physique he wanted, he could wean himself off. He looked at how this guy had an amazing body and he thought he would try some.

He put an order in and explained that he didn't want his friend Jake to know, so not to approach him when Jake was around. They devised a signal that meant the guy had what he wanted, and to meet after they had been to the gym somewhere discrete. Dylan was nervous, excited, and worried. After all, this was against the law.

Anabolic steroids are a class C drug, and it is illegal to possess them. A sentence of up to fourteen years can be given if caught.

Dylan began on a very low dose, and he felt fine. He took advice on how to take it from the guy at the gym. He was told to increase it slowly, then after a couple of months to stop it altogether, to give his system a rest. This is known as cycling. It's thought to be safer to take it this way.

The drugs began to do their work, increasing his muscle mass and decreasing his body fat. Dylan was pleased with the results. It wasn't long before Jake and his mates at the pub began to notice a difference. The jokes didn't stop - it just changed to calling him names like 'Popeye.' Dylan didn't mind this so much and would joke along with them. Jake began to get concerned for his friend though as he thought Dylan was unnaturally muscley. He asked him in a joking manner, "are you taking something? Because you honestly don't look right, mate." Dylan denied it but it made him take another look at himself. He realised he was looking very different, but he liked it. He didn't want to go back to being what they described as 'the runt.'

Dylan noticed his skin was becoming inflamed and he had spots. Jake told him he was snappy and not his usual jovial self. Dylan mentioned this to the guy at the gym and he told him it was probably time to give it a break from taking the pills. He also suggested that in a couple of weeks, he may want to build up to having the drugs injected. He told him that this is what he and several others at the gym did. Dylan was worried about doing this so said he would think about it.

Following a rest period, Dylan began to take the drug again. He noticed when he stopped taking it, he was even more moody, and was getting terrible headaches. Now he was back on them, these symptoms slowly went away.

Dylan was hooked, anabolic steroids are *addictive* and the guy at the gym had a nice little business going - selling the illegal drugs to the vulnerable people who only wanted to improve their appearance.

Dylan kept taking the anabolic steroids for over a year and he wasn't sure if it was a side effect, but his hair was falling out. Dylan didn't have all the side effects that taking anabolic steroids can have, but he definitely noticed some of them.

Here is a list of side effects for men that may result from taking anabolic steroids, found on the NHS website at the end of this chapter.

- Reduced sperm count.
- Infertility.
- Shrunken testicals.
- Erectile dysfunction.
- Hair loss.
- Breast development.
- Increased risk of prostate cancer.
- Severe acne.
- Stomach pain.

Effects of taking anabolic steroids for women include:

- Facial hair growth.
- Loss of breast tissue.

- Swelling of the clitoris.
- Deepening of the voice.
- Increased sex drive.
- Problems with periods.
- Hair loss.
- Severe acne.

Both men and women can develop any of the following:

- Heart attack or stroke.
- Liver or kidney failure.
- Blood clots.
- Fluid retention.
- High cholesterol.
- High blood pressure.

Psychological effects can be:

- Aggressive behaviour.
- Mood swings.
- Paranoia.
- Manic behaviour.
- Hallucinations and delusions.

Dylan loved his new looks and he noticed the ladies were paying him more attention. Jake had always been the ladies' man and Dylan was elated when he got some of the attention. However, Jake became increasingly concerned for his friend, so decided to make some enquires at the gym. It wasn't long before he found out the anabolic steroids were being sold at the gym and further investigation led him to the guy who was dealing to his friend. He didn't want to approach the man because he was worried that there may be repercussions for Dylan. He decided to speak with Dylan and tell him what he had found out.

Dylan was defensive at first but then realised that Jake was only being a good mate and was genuinely concerned about his health. Jake told Dylan he was in danger of serious side effects, and he asked him to go to the doctor to get help in coming off the drugs. He also offered to change the gym they went to so they could avoid seeing the guy who supplied the drugs.

Dylan knew Jake would be a great support, but he desperately didn't want to go back to looking how he used to. He told Jake he felt ashamed that he had resorted to taking the anabolic steroids. He also explained how he felt ridiculed by the other lads, and he didn't want to go back to feeling like that. Jake told him he would help in any way he could.

Dylan went to see his doctor and was surprised at how understanding he was. He spoke at length with Dylan about the side effects, but most importantly he listened to why Dylan began taking the drugs. He told Dylan he may have body dysmorphia. He explained that the side effects of coming off the drugs would be unpleasant but that if he didn't come off them, he would be in danger of developing irreversible and possibly fatal damage to his body. The doctor told Dylan he would need to see a specially trained counsellor who would help Dylan through the detox programme.

Vanity and insecurity were the main reasons that Dylan began to take the anabolic steroids. It would be difficult for him to detox and to adjust to being his authentic self. Dylan needs to learn self-love and to appreciate his good health.

Further advice can be found in the links on this website:

www.nhs.uk/conditions/anabolic-steroid-misuse/

LYN'S
STORY

MELANOMA CANCER

Laying on her sun lounger in Palma, Majorca, Lyn sipped her mojito. She had gone on holiday with her friend, June. They were both widows and they loved their holidays in the sun. The ladies enjoyed several holidays a year, always in the sun.

Lyn felt better when she had a tan. When she was younger, she would hire a sun bed for weeks at a time. She always moisturised her skin and she wore sunscreen. However, if the sun wasn't too strong, she sometimes went without sunscreen, because a tan was always her aim.

Lyn had pale skin and fair hair. She hated her pale skin and always felt so much better with a tan. She also felt that the sun gave her a boost somehow. According to **www.womenshealthmag.com**, Dr. Catherine Shaffer, Ph.D., UV exposure releases beta-endorphins in the body, which bind to opioid receptors-neurotransmitters that signal pain relief in your brain. Therefore, sunlight may create that temporary 'feel good' sensation.

Lyn doesn't work as her husband left her with enough money to be able to enjoy life without the need to work. She has four grown up children who all agree that Mum should enjoy life. They were all heart broken when Barry, Lyn's husband, died at the age of fifty. He was six years Lyn's senior and he worshiped Lyn. He ensured that she never had to work. She was happy staying home with the children, and he earned enough to take care of them all, and that was how they liked it.

Lyn loved to sit in their beautiful garden during the summer months. As soon as 'the sun had his hat on,' Lyn was out on the lounger. She noticed when the autumn came, she began to feel down, so she inevitably booked a holiday in the sun. A winter holiday gave her something to look forward to also. Lyn took every opportunity to sunbathe. Even her hobbies involved being outdoors. She enjoyed playing golf and crown green bowls. She had made some good friends and occasionally went on walking holidays with some of the ladies.

Sun has some positive and many negative effects for humans. The skin requires exposure to UV-B rays in order to stimulate vitamin D synthesis. A lack of vitamin D can cause rickets.

Lyn and June were getting ready for an evening out on their holiday in Palma, Majorca, when June noticed a mole on Lyn's back. She pointed it out to Lyn and Lyn said, "oh I've had that for ages, you've never noticed it before?" June advised her to get it checked out when they got home. Lyn thought she would get her daughter to take a look at it.

On their return Lyn was busy with her hobbies and catching up with other friends. She completely forgot about the mole on her back. The summer months flew by, and Lyn had a holiday booked for two weeks at the end of October. She was going with June again, this time to Cuba. The ladies enjoyed several shopping trips to prepare for the holiday. During one of these trips, June remembered Lyn's mole. She asked if she had had it checked and Lyn told her she had forgotten about it. Promising to go to her doctor when they returned from the next holiday, June was reassured. However, while on holiday, June was shocked to see quite a difference to the mole on Lyn's back. She didn't want to spoil the holiday or to frighten Lyn, but she did tell Lyn that the mole was bigger. They put it out of their minds and continued to have a great holiday.

Chatting over a drink one evening, Lyn admitted she was getting a little concerned about the mole, so she asked June if she would take a photo of it when they returned to their room. June obliged and when Lyn saw the photo, she wondered what all the fuss was about. She laughed and told June that Barry used to say she had a beauty spot on her back. Lyn once again put the subject of the mole out of her mind.

The holiday was amazing; they had gone on boat trips, horse riding, and walked up the Dunn's River Falls. Returning home always made Lyn feel a little down, but she did look forward to seeing the family.

Lyn was more tanned than usual on her return this time and her daughter remarked on it. Lyn said the weather was extremely hot. Her daughter asked whether Lyn had used a high factor sunscreen and Lyn said she used factor 15 which was higher than she usually wore. Lyn thought while they were talking about her skin, she would mention the mole on her back. Her daughter looked and told Lyn to go to the doctor as soon as possible because from what she had read, it looked nasty.

Lyn phoned for an appointment the next day. At worst she thought the Doctor would remove it, so when the doctor said she needed to see a dermatologist, she was shocked. He took a full history and explained to Lyn that she should have had it checked when it was first noticed.

The doctor explained that while a tan may look nice, the golden colour is due to damage to the top layer of your skin. Lyn did say that because the weather was so hot, she did burn a few times. The doctor asked whether her skin was red or whether it blistered. She told him it was red a few times but that it did blister once. She told him she put after-sun cream on and after a couple of days, the blisters went away.

The doctor went on to tell Lyn that she had given herself first degree burns when her skin was red, but that the blisters were second degree burns. This damage is deeper and may involve nerve endings. The doctor gave Lyn a leaflet about being safe in the sun. The leaflet also covered the subject of premature aging. It made Lyn think about the damage she had done over the years to achieve a tan. She promised herself that she would wear a very high factor sunscreen on her face from now on.

Two weeks later, Lyn had her appointment with the dermatologist. Once again, Lyn thought the mole would be removed and that would be the end of it. The dermatologist looked closely at the mole and asked Lyn if she had noticed it change. Lyn explained that as it was on her back, it was difficult for her to monitor it. However, since her friend had taken a photograph of it on holiday, she had asked her daughter to take some photos.

Over a period of a couple of months, Lyn had noticed a difference. She told the dermatologist that the mole had become darker and larger, but other than that she found it difficult to tell. She said it was not painful and if her friend hadn't said anything about it, she may never have known it was there. She did tell her the tale about her husband saying she had a beauty spot and they used to joke about it. Her dermatologist explained that because of the changes and length of time she'd had it, she wanted to remove it that day to send a sample to the laboratory. She told Lyn she would do it using a local anaesthetic and that it would be tender for a few days. She also warned Lyn that it had the appearance of a melanoma.

Melanoma is a type of skin cancer often caused by too much sun exposure from either a sun bed or the sun. The dermatologist told Lyn, the sooner this type of skin cancer is detected and subsequently treated, the better the outcome.

The results came back and unfortunately it was melanoma. Lyn would need to see the dermatologist to discuss further treatment. Lyn was informed she needed to see a plastic surgeon who would remove a wider area of skin to make sure no cancer cells were left behind. She would also require a sentinel node biopsy to see if the melanoma had spread to the lymph nodes. Lyn would have to go to hospital as a day case and be prepared to stay overnight as this procedure is done under general anaesthetic.

The sun can cause many other skin problems but not many people realise that cataracts can be caused by the sun.

Lyn was in a high-risk group of developing skin cancer. Certain things can increase your chance of developing melanoma such as:

- Lots of moles or freckles.
- Pale skin that burns easily.
- Red or blonde hair.
- Close family member who's had melanoma.
- Blue eyes.
- Previously damaged skin through sun burn or radiotherapy.
- Previous diagnosis of skin cancer.
- Being older.

With the support of her family and friends, Lyn underwent treatment and was eventually given the all-clear. She swore she would stay in the shade from now on. But she found it very difficult and sometimes needed reminding by friends and family. Her days of lazing in the sun were over but Lyn actually found that her complexion improved. She was using very high factor sunscreen and found herself encouraging others to do the same.

Lyn realises she has had a narrow escape and is grateful to everyone who helped her through the treatment. She admits it's not easy and that she has changed the way she looks at enjoying her holidays.

Her and June tend to go when it's not so hot or to new exciting places they hadn't dreamt of going before, where the sun is not the main attraction. She wears a hat when she plays bowls and golf. Her friends have all learned from Lyn's experience and now wear sunscreen and a hat.

Lyn realises that she shouldn't have ignored June's advice about getting her mole checked out as soon as possible.

She knows the outcome could have been very different and is grateful for every day.

Resources for learning more about Melanoma cancer:

www.womenshealthmag.com
www.macmillan.org.uk/melanoma

OWN YOUR HEALTH

Human beings are so complex. We never really know what someone else is thinking or feeling.

Psychiatrists all over the world would love to get inside the head of their patients.

We all feel emotions. None of them are good or bad emotions, they are just emotions. They simply occur as a response to something or someone. We can feel sad about a situation, an emotion we hope won't last.

Anger is an emotion that is usually short-term; however, in some cases it can consume people.

Happiness and sheer **joy** are wonderful emotions we would all love to feel every day.

Being **afraid** or **ashamed** are emotions we will inevitably feel at some point in our lives. These emotions are part of what makes us human. We are programmed from birth. We listen to both praise and criticism.

As we go through the journey of life, we gather skills to help us deal with trauma, heartbreak, and failure. We gain belief systems. Some can be beneficial, some detrimental. We learn to listen to our inner voice and if your inner voice is telling you that you are worthless because of your conditioning as a child, you tend to believe this.

However, if your conditioning had positive reinforcement and you were made to believe you had worth and were loved, you believe this. These beliefs often set the tone for our lives and develop our personalities. Certain things we were conditioned to believe as children were for protection, for example 'don't talk to strangers,' or 'don't eat junk food.'

As adults, most of us (especially if you are a parent) put others before ourselves. I believe at times, whether knowingly or not, we have all harmed ourselves. We need to learn to love ourselves.

Self-love is not selfish. It means we can live another day to help someone else. It means we can enable ourselves to become stronger and a better person. This in return can only serve to help others.

During the covid 19 pandemic we saw dreadful pictures on the news of health care workers on their knees with exhaustion.

We need to take care of the carers to enable them to take care of us when we need it most. This is true of ourselves too. Often, we can see when someone else needs to have a break or take time out for themselves, so why can't we see it when we need it ourselves? Why do we push ourselves to the point of no return at times? Why do we feel guilty for doing something good for ourselves?

For the vast majority of us, it stems back to childhood. The way we were brought up. For example, when you do take time for yourself, you feel guilty because you were conditioned to think you must always be busy.

Sometimes having a chat with a friend may be just what you need. Other times you really may need to get away from it all - leave everything behind and switch off. It's important that we learn to recognise these needs in both ourselves as well as others. It could just save someone's life.

We all have things in life that we cannot change but life can become messy, and it may help to have some strategies to help you cope.

I find if I write things down and put things in some sense of order or priority, it can help. Look at things you can change to make life easier, less stressful, maybe less confrontational. Learn ways you can be calmer, don't let the little things get you down. Be patient with yourself and others. Don't let others disrespect you. Keep calm. If you go off like a bottle of pop, you can guarantee the other person will raise their voice even higher. However, if someone else is enraged and raising their voice, you will notice that if you remain calm, they will eventually soften their voice and maybe then you can reason with them.

Walking away from conflict and trying to resolve it another day is better than battling it out when both people are angry. It's important to remember it is not someone else's responsibility to look after your health. You should be in partnership with your health professional, not expect them to make you better.

I believe we have a responsibility to ourselves and others to take care of our health.

Self-preservation comes in many forms but essentially it comes down to taking a step back from the situation, whether that is self -harm, addiction, abuse, or plain self-destructive behaviour. Take time to consider your behaviour and then act appropriately to get back on the right track.

As we have seen in some of the scenarios, vanity can cause us to act irresponsibly. We may not realise that we have a disorder like body-dysmorphia. Maybe we need to learn to listen to our closest friends and family as well as ourselves?

Some might say "if you can't love yourself, you can't love anyone else." Plan some special time. We all enjoy different things; some activities are weather-dependent, or you may have commitments. Whatever you decide to do to relax or destress, make sure it is sustainable and that it gives you pleasure.

Enjoy the planning stage. For example, make a graph or pie chart indicating the percentage of pleasure each activity gives you. You may even want to replicate this for places you enjoy visiting - even down to the people you enjoy spending time with.

The more you think about all the wonderful things you enjoy, the happier you will be.

It is important to recognise in yourself and others when to ask for help. Don't sink into that black hole or allow someone you love to do the same.

Ask for help, most people want to help. When you become overwhelmed, it is not a weakness to ask for help. It is a strength. Very few people can pull themselves from the depths of despair. When you are fully recovered, you may want to help others. Think about volunteering or being that special friend to someone. Because you have been through a trying time, you will recognise the signs to look out for. So be there for someone. Being there for someone in their time of need is so rewarding. Here are some ideas to help you feel better and more in control of your life.

These are just suggestions, and you may have some of your own. I would start slowly because you don't want to be overwhelmed. It may be a good idea to go with someone if you are the type to feel embarrassed or awkward meeting people:

- Go outside, be with nature.
- Dance to your favourite tune like nobody is watching.
- Watch a really good film.
- Go for a drive and sing at the top of your voice.
- Switch off from everything electrical for a day.
- Go for a walk, anywhere.
- Plan a weekend away.
- Have your favourite food and really savour it.
- Punch a pillow to relieve stress.
- Stroke your pet and tell them your troubles.
- Speak to a friend.
- De-clutter (if that floats your boat).
- Escape in a book or magazine.
- Do a puzzle (word, sudoku, jigsaw etc).
- Treat yourself to a facial or massage.
- If you are religious, spend some time praying or go to your place of worship.
- Plan an evening with your favourite people.

- Take a long luxurious bath.

- Sit by the sea and watch the waves.

- Be creative; knit, paint, crotchet, write a poem or do some DIY.

- Join a yoga class or a sport you enjoy, or something you have never tried before.

Whatever you decide to do to treat yourself, make sure it is something YOU enjoy doing. Live each day as if it were your, last.

Love life, people, and places. Give yourself a break. Take each day as a fresh start; you may not have been so good with your decisions yesterday, but today you are so lucky because you get to try again.

Respect yourself and others. Be kind to yourself and others. Most of all, love yourself. You are unique and very special.